HERBS FROM THE BIBLE

by Patricia Armstrong

Published by
Amberwood Publishing Ltd
Rochester, England

PLANTLIFE

Registered Charity No. 1059559
enquiries@plantlife.org.uk

Support Plantlife International, the wild plant conservation charity
dedicated exclusively to conserving all forms of plant life in their
natural habitats in the UK, Europe and across the world.

ISBN 1-899308-29-6

Cover design by Studio Read

Printed in Great Britain by Kent Art Printers who use
environmentally friendly production methods. The inks used have been
derived from a vegetable (not mineral oil) base, and the booklet has been
printed using "alcohol-free" dampening for dramatically reduced Volatile
Organic Compound (VOC) Emissions. The power used in the print
production of this booklet has been supplied by Ecotricity.

CONTENTS

About the Author

Patricia Armstrong was once heard to say that, in the unlikely event of her ever writing a book she would call it 'Quite by Chance', since everything in her life up to that point seemed to have happened unexpectedly and counter to any plans she had made. Many years and several books later, that title has never been used because she ceased to believe in chance a long time ago. Perhaps 'The Hand of God in Everything' would be more appropriate now.

Patricia admits that her credentials for writing such a book as 'Herbs from the Bible' are poor, but hopes that going on record as a committed Christian, an ecumenically-minded Catholic, a lover of the Bible and a Secular Franciscan will mitigate any lack of scholarship.

Coming from a background of 'orthodox medicine' (nurse married to a surgeon), Patricia has learned to integrate knowledge of pharmacology with the more ancient arts/crafts of phytotherapy and pharmacognosy. It has been a fascinating journey from drugs to herbs and she has enjoyed every moment of it.

Patricia's Patron Saint, Francis of Assisi – who is also the Patron Saint of ecology – would surely approve. He understood the connectedness of all Creation, calling Sun and Moon, Water and Fire and even Death his brothers and sisters. And Francis knew how to praise:

> 'All powerful, most holy, most high and supreme God,
> all good, supreme good, total good, you who alone are good:
> we give you praise, all glory, all thanks, all honour,
> all blessing and every good.
> So be it. So be it.'
>
> Amen

Foreword

Two of the most important influences on my life have been the Bible and my scientific study of medicinal plants. Both of these areas are now, sadly, minority interests in twenty first century Britain; although both have shown amazing resilience in surviving thus far and I believe that neither will ever be completely lost. From the Bible, we have, of course, the words of Jesus Himself that 'Heaven and earth may pass away but my words will never pass away'.

I was very interested to read this book and to see how the medicinal plants mentioned in the Bible are used as a framework for telling its themes and stories in a very readable and racy manner. It is important that such topics be made readable since it is a lamentable fact that, nowadays, even many committed Christians have not come to grips with reading the Bible as a whole. Consequently they have little idea of the threads of thought and the unfolding revelation of God and His ways which can be seen by doing this. Patricia Armstrong pulls out the main ideas in a colloquial and attractive style which kept me reading over two long train journeys.

Many people will be surprised at the number of medicinal plants mentioned in the Bible which still have a place in current herbal therapy. One of the titles of Yahweh (Jehovah to older readers – and singers at Welsh rugby matches!), the Hebrew God of the Covenant, is 'I am the God who heals you' and this book reminds us that God has provided means of healing in his creation, as well as the more supernatural miracles of healing which He still performs even today. It has always interested me that Paul, writing to Timothy, recommends him to drink some wine for his tender stomach rather than offering only to pray for him. This, together with some other instances, such as the poultice of figs used to treat Hezekiah's boil, reminds us that healing is not an either God/or medicine situation but that all healing comes from God. As a practising

Christian and a health professional, I have no problem in praying for people to be healed by God and their also seeking advice from doctors and taking medicines and undergoing surgery. The comments on the findings of scientific research on many of the herbs also remind us that part of the way in which we are made in the image of God is to use our creativeness and ingenuity in developing and exploiting (in the best meaning of the word) the materials that he has provided in nature.

The variety of plants mentioned also shows the lavishness of God and his love of diversity. Study of creation is one way in which we sense and discover something about God but we find out much more about Him from reading the Bible. I hope that this book will stimulate all who read it to do both and start, or carry on with, the greatest adventure in the world – that of getting to know God.

Peter Houghton
Professor in Pharmacognosy, Department of Pharmacy, King's College, London

Acknowledgements

Great gratitude is due to all those who have made researching and writing this book such a delight. Some are long dead, of course, which only proves how our work, our actions and our influence continue throughout future generations we shall never live to see. I doubt if either Dioscorides or Pliny the Elder dreamt of such respectful recognition some two thousand years after their observations and writings.

All biblical quotations are from the New International Version, unless otherwise stated in the text. The New Jerusalem Bible was the source for the apocryphal Book of Judith, for the story of that beautiful seductress with her gruesome picnic basket, and the Authorized King James Version (KJAV) took me back to wonderful poetic language remembered from my youth.

For Michael Zohary, the Holy Land was home and he wrote his book *Plants of the Bible* while Professor of Botany at Jerusalem University. Tom Ratcliffe spent time there on his retirement as fulfilment of a lifelong dream, and his book *Bible Plants, Fruit & Products* is the happy result of that visit. I have quoted them both liberally, absorbing some of their enthusiasm and love of plants and Scripture as I did so.

Another botanist – Christopher Whitehouse of the Royal Horticultural Society, Wisley – answered my sometimes strange questions ('What makes Stinging Nettles sting?' and 'What's the difference between Milk Thistle and Holy Thistle?') with unfailing patience and good humour.

Andrew Chevallier and Professor Edzard Ernst have provided most valuable work on herbs in modern medicine, and I am grateful for their permission to use some of that work here.

My friend and mentor, Father Ignatius Kelly, ofm, Franciscan theologian, has given enormous encouragement throughout the writing of this book. It has been his task to keep me, if not on the paths of righteousness, at least away from heresy. He shares my own brand of humour, and I thank God for him.

Finally, I really must thank June Crisp and Vic Perfitt of *Bio-Health*, not only for suggesting that I write a book based on lectures that Vic had already given, but also for their infectious enthusiasm for herbs. They have opened up a new world for me.

Note to Reader

Whilst the author has made every effort to ensure that the contents of this book are accurate in every particular, it is not intended to be regarded as a substitute for professional medical advice under treatment. Readers are urged to give careful consideration to any difficulties which they may be experiencing with their own health and to consult their General Practitioner if uncertain as to its cause or nature. Neither the author nor the publisher can accept any legal responsibility for any health problem which results from use of the self-help methods described.

1 | Introduction

'In the beginning God created . . .'

The story told in Genesis – the Old Testament book whose very name means 'origin' – is so familiar to Christians, to Jews and to Moslems that we are in danger of forgetting the awesome power of the One who brought everything into being; the diversity and playfulness of his imagination (contrast a flea with, say, a giraffe; the massive Californian Redwood with a blade of grass) and the depth of his love for his creation.

Julian of Norwich, the 14th century mystic, in one of her 'shewings' (visions) wrote: 'God showed me a little thing, no bigger than a hazelnut lying in the palm of my hand, and it was as round as a ball. As I gazed at it, I thought, "What can this be?" And God said, "It is all of creation." I was amazed that it could survive, it was so small, but again God spoke to me: "It lasts both now and always, because I cherish it." And so everything receives its being from the love of God.

'In this little thing I saw three truths: the first is that God made it, the second is that God loves it, and the third is that God keeps it.'

The rich pageant of people across the pages of the Old Testament knew God as Creator, Lover and Keeper – patriarchs, judges, prophets, priests, kings, seers and sages, law and history writers, poets and musicians and ordinary people. So did the authors of the New Testament, who bring us the life of Jesus of Nazareth, Son of God, fulfilment of the old Covenant between God and His people. In the gospels, in the 'Acts of the Apostles', in letters to the early Church and in the apocalyptic writings of the Book of Revelation they reveal to us the new Covenant between God and his people.

In the great 'library' which we call the Bible, herbs play a significant part. They speak of God's love and care for us: feeding us, healing us, enhancing life for us with their scents and flavours and dyes and calling us to holiness and worship. Herbs symbolize perfection in relationships, in peace and justice, and much, much more. But, for the moment, back to the beginning . . .

GENESIS CH 1:11-13

'Then God said, "Let the land produce vegetation: seed-bearing plants and trees on the land that bear fruit with seed in it, according to their various kinds." And it was so. The land produced vegetation: plants bearing seed according to their kinds and trees bearing fruit with seed in it according to their kinds. And God saw that it was good. And there was evening, and there was morning – the third day.'

GENESIS CH 1:27-31

'So God created man in his own image, in the image of God he created him; male and female he created them. God blessed them and said to them, "Be fruitful and increase in number; fill the earth and subdue it. Rule over the fish of the sea and the birds of the air and over every creature that moves on the ground."

Then God said, "I give you every seed bearing plant on the face of the whole earth And every tree that has fruit with seed in it. They will be yours for food.

And to all the beasts of the earth and all the birds of the air and all the creatures that move on the ground – everything that has the breath of life in it – I give every green plant for food." And it was so. God saw all that he had made and it was very good. And there was evening, and there was morning – the sixth day.'

Writing this book has been a voyage of discovery for me, as I hope it will be for those who read it. The book itself has 'evolved' since its tentative beginnings as a result of a chance telephone conversation with June Crisp about a successful series of lectures on biblical herbs given by Vic Perfitt. This really is their book – I simply took up the idea of putting herbs and Bible stories together and wrote it, and so thoroughly enjoyed doing it that it never seemed like work. In fact, like Mark (see the introduction to the section on the gospels), sometimes the stories became so exciting and so 'now' that I slipped from past to present – which seemed so right for me at the time of writing that I have not changed that in editing.

Herbal medicine is as old as man himself. From earliest times man and medicine have, of necessity, developed together. Man was first hunter-gatherer, then farmer. As hunter-gatherer, he was skilled in recognising herbs, berries, barks and roots, not only for food, but also to cure his ills. As farmer, man cultivated plants for food, and his crafting of herbs for medicinal as well as culinary purposes has continued through the ages. Herbal medicine is, and always has been, inextricably interwoven with anthropology, botany, the medical sciences, agriculture and horticulture.

Today, in 2004, it is worth reminding ourselves that eighty per cent of the world's population still rely upon plants for their primary source of medication, and that even in our more 'sophisticated' western cultures, twenty-five per cent of all prescription drugs are still derived from plants, or are copies of plant molecules isolated from various species. These facts indicate the importance of plants in our everyday life for preventing and for treating adverse conditions that affect us all. It is remarkable to realise that the most important life-saving drugs have been developed from plant material. Conditions as diverse as heart disease, leukaemia and ovarian cancer are treated with drugs whose origins lie in herbs, not to mention pain relief and the many other life-threatening disorders. Even as I write, there is news of further exciting research, and it is so good to see highly qualified medical practitioners working with the best brains in phyto-therapy to pool their knowledge and expertise against all the scourges of disease to which human flesh is heir.

I have been given forty herbs with which to roam through the Bible; so let us begin at the beginning and proceed to the end – from Genesis to Revelation. The book itself falls into nine sections, six in the Old Testament and three in the New Testament. Within each of those sections (each one of which has an explanatory foreword) there are herbs with their botany, their folklore and their modern medicinal or culinary properties, accompanied by an appropriate Bible story. In this way I hope the story has been told of God's growing relationship with his people through the ages. One thing is certain, neither herbs nor the Bible are ever boring!

THE
OLD
TESTAMENT

2 | The Pentateuch

The first five books of the Bible form the *Torah* – the Law of Israel. Pentateuch means, simply, 'five scrolls' and they span a period of some 600 years (from *c*1900BC to *c*1250BC), although it is impossible to date them with any accuracy.

In these five books – Genesis, Exodus, Leviticus, Numbers and Deuteronomy – we find the beginnings of God's relationship with his creation. But this most holy God never divulges his name. The nearest the Israelites ever came was *Yahweh*, the totally inadequate translation of which is '*I Am*'. In those days, God chose patriarchs to lay the foundations of the nation he had called to be holy, as he was holy. In those days, God spoke to men in many different ways – in visions and dreams, by angel messengers in human form, and even, sometimes, directly, although no man could look at God and survive the experience.

The Pentateuch has a tremendous 'introduction' in the Creation story, after which we read of the account of God's chosen people, from the call of Abraham to the death of Moses. These primitive, nomadic people are led gradually to know the God who is unknowable, to trust him and to rely on him in any circumstances. They are given laws and a social structure. They are given a covenant, which commits them to fidelity to their God, in return for which he is their protector and provider. They break faith often; God never does.

Genesis is nothing if not action-packed. In the first eleven chapters we find Creation; The Fall of Man and his banishment from Eden; The First Murder (Cain killing his brother Abel in a fit of jealous rage); The Flood, and Noah with his ark full of animals (followed by a new start and God's promise not to destroy everything on earth ever again), and the Tower of Babel (where God confuses the language of the world and scatters people over the face of the whole earth when they get too far above themselves).

In chapter twelve we meet the great patriarch, Abraham, whose descendants will form God's own people, and it is at this point that God's relationship with those he has chosen becomes more individual and intimate. Genesis takes the story on through several generations, finishing with the death of Joseph, Abraham's great-grandson, in Egypt.

Exodus might just as easily have been called 'The Book of Moses', that giant of a character who dominates the scene throughout. From the most unlikely background, it is Moses who leads the Israelites out of captivity in Egypt. Through Moses, God gives the Law to the people of Israel. It is with Moses that God speaks 'Face to face, as a man might speak with a friend'. Exodus is an epic; it is the story of the birth of a nation.

Leviticus is basically a rule book which takes its name from the priestly families, the Levites, who were concerned in building the Tabernacle in the Tent of Meeting in the desert, and the Levitical priests who administered the Law. Through Moses, God gave the gift of priesthood to Aaron, his sons and his descendants in perpetuity.

Israel was committed to 'blind' obedience to God in all the rituals and rules he gave them, but now, in our own day, we are able to see that these were essential for the health and well-being of that more primitive people. They would have known nothing of the need for such rigid hygiene in that hot climate, or for the importance of quarantine in time of epidemic, or for preventative measures against disease. Here we see God looking after his people simply by enforcing his natural laws.

The awesomeness of God shines through this book. He is way beyond the experience of his 'creatures', but he longs for them to be holy, as he is holy.

Numbers begins with a census, taken when the Israelites have been wandering about in the desert for a couple of years (which is why the book is called Numbers). It begins soon after the escape from captivity in Egypt and ends on the eve of entry into the land of Canaan – the land flowing with milk and honey – thirty-eight years later.

There is some overlap with material in other books, particularly of Exodus, and it is a sad fact that Moses who has led the Israelites in all those years in the desert, who has been allowed to see the Promised Land from a mountain top, is not going to live to enter it.

Deuteronomy is a second version of the Law. It was lost for a time and was only found during refurbishment of the Temple at the time of King Josiah in 622BC. The king did great penance when it was found, because the people had wandered so far from God, and the Law was reinstated forthwith.

But now the Israelites are gathered on the Plain of Moab, ready to enter Canaan. Moses speaks to them, reminding them of all God has done for them in the past forty years. He exhorts them to keep God's holy laws, so that God's goodness will remain with them. Moses speaks of God's love and his desire to be loved by his people in return.

In Deuteronomy, the laws written in Exodus, Leviticus and Numbers are reiterated and gathered together to provide a social and religious structure for the different, more settled life the Israelites will be living in Canaan.

Oak ~ *(Quercus ithaburensis. also Q. calliprinos also Q. aegilops)*

Plant description

There are so many different oak trees that it is difficult to know where begin, and there is certainly no room to mention them all here. The English Oak (*Quercus robur*) is common throughout Europe (except the far north) and it varies enormously in size and shape. However its bark (ridged and grey), its catkins (both male and female), its acorns (pedunculated), and its leaves (deeply lobed) are familiar in woods and the oak sometimes stands in solitary grandeur, marking the boundary of a field. The English Oak is deciduous. A mature oak wood is a nature reserve in miniature: bats will roost in a hollow trunk; nuthatches, tree-creepers, woodpeckers – green and spotted – will take advantage of its sanctuary for nests; unimaginable numbers of insects and beetles will live, move and have their being in its bark; its leaves will provide food and shelter for innumerable caterpillars; its acorns will provide winter food for squirrels and jays, and it will always be a symbol of strength and endurance for all who see it, for it grows to a very great age.

The Holm Oak (*Quercus ilex*) is evergreen and impressive both in height (up to 25m) and in the grand shape of its dome. The bark is craggy – almost black; its male catkins long and conspicuous; its acorns sessile; its leaves dark and glossy, long and narrow.

However, it is the oaks of the Holy Land that particularly interest us here, and we must turn to the experts, Zohary and Ratcliffe to identify these for us: Zohary says that of the three oak species in the thickets and forests of the Holy Land, two of them, the common evergreen oak (the Holm Oak) and the Tabor oak are the most impressive in their stature, age and dominance. Ratcliffe identifies the deciduous oak as *Quercus aegilops* (or *Q. ithaburensis*) and the evergreen oak as *Quercus coccifera* (or *Q. ilex*).

Both Zohary and Ratcliffe agree that the Hebrew *allon* and *elon* refer to the oak and that 'elah' or 'ayil' do not. I only mention this because it gave rise to confusion in early translations of the Bible and references to some trees were erroneous. Also, we shall be looking at a different sort of 'oak' in the story of David and Absalom much later – the Terebinth.

Plant Lore

The oak was thought to be sacred to the gods of thunder (the Roman Jupiter, the Greek Zeus, the Scandinavian Thor) because it was struck by lightning so often.

The oak has been honoured in poetry ('Those green-robed senators of mighty woods – Keats' 'Hyperion' Book I), in proverb (Oak before Ash, only a splash. Ash before Oak, expect a soak), and in song ('Heart of Oak' – a sea song referring to the timber used to build ships and to celebrate victories at sea in the mid-eighteenth century). It is said to have taken several thousand mature oak trees growing over some 900 acres to build just one three-tier battleship at that time.

And swathes of oak forest must have been stripped bare to provide rafters, richly carved pews and choir stalls and sculpted cladding for baptismal fonts in hundreds of churches and cathedrals.

'The Major Oak' in Sherwood Forest is said to have been a mature tree in the time of Robin Hood (early 13th century) and as many as a dozen adults can stand comfortably in its now hollow trunk. Robin Hood often used hollow oak trunks as holding places for the deer he poached in the forest, one tree being dubbed 'Robin Hood's Larder'. (That particular tree was burned down in the mid-20th century when schoolgirls lit a fire inside it to boil water for their picnic!)

'The Ladies' Race' run at Epsom in Surrey after the Derby and called 'The Oaks' was named from Lord Derby's estate of that name at its inauguration in 1779.

'The King Oak' in Windsor Great Park in which William the Conqueror is supposed to have sheltered (1066) still stands with its girth of some 11m.

Interestingly, oak and holly together denote hospitality. Abraham's Holm ('holly') Oak at Mamre is depicted in Rublev's 'Trinity' icon, which is also called 'The Hospitality of Abraham'.

Also in biblical times, oak trees marked burial sites and landmarks, as well as being a popular medium for carving idols.

Uses in modern herbal medicine

Oak is a powerful astringent, mildly invigorating and antiseptic. Mixed with aromatics, it is a useful weapon against chronic diarrhoea.

A decoction made from Oak bark makes an effective gargle for sore throats. It also provides a good treatment for leucorrhoea and for bleeding haemorrhoids.

'AND SARAH LAUGHED'

After the chaos of the Tower of Babel quite a long time passes before we come to one of the great defining moments in the Old Testament: God calls Abram, a descendant of Noah, and simply tells him to leave his father's house, and his people, and his country and to go to an unspecified land with the promise that he (God) will make Abram into a great nation with a great name and that he (Abram) will be blessed.

Amazingly, Abram doesn't ask any questions; he just does as he is told and leaves. 'Abram took his wife Sarai, his nephew Lot, all the possessions they had accumulated and the people they had accumulated in Haran, and they set out for the land of Canaan, and they arrived there.' (Genesis 12:5)

Abram continued to travel through the land. At the great Oak of Moreh at Shechem God appeared to Abram again and promised that his offspring would inherit the land, so Abram built an altar there. He built another between Bethel and Ai before setting out for the Negev. But there came a severe famine to the land and Abram and his retinue had to travel down to Egypt to find food and water.

Abram might have been a man close to God, obedient and devout, but he was far from perfect. Sarai, his wife, was a beautiful woman and Abram knew that if Pharoah set eyes on her he would want her, and he might well kill to get her. So Abram passed Sarai off as his sister, and when Pharaoh took Sarai into his palace Abram was treated well too, receiving gifts of sheep and cattle and donkeys and camels and servants. Unfortunately for Abram, God took a dim view of all this and sent disease on Pharaoh's house, and when Pharaoh found out the truth he threw them out of Egypt.

And so Abram went back with Sarai and Lot and all his belongings, retracing his steps to the place where he had first built an altar: 'There Abram called on the name of the Lord.' As well he might.

Both Abram and Lot were wealthy men; they both had flocks and herds and tents, but the land couldn't support them while they stayed together in one place. Their herdsmen began to quarrel and life became miserable, so Abram suggested that they part company. He gave Lot first choice of direction, and Lot chose the whole fertile plain of Jordan and set out towards the east. 'Abram lived in Canaan, while Lot lived among the cities of the plain and pitched his tents near Sodom.' Not a good choice, Lot!

When Lot had left, God said to Abram, "Lift up your eyes and look north and south, east and west. All the land that you see I will give to you and your offspring for ever. I will make your offspring like the dust of the earth, so that if anyone could count the dust, then your offspring could be counted. Go walk through the length and breadth of the land, for I am giving it to you."

So Abram moved his tents and went to live near the great oaks of Mamre at Hebron, and there he built an altar to the Lord' (Genesis 13:14-18)

Abram was getting restive, and no wonder. God kept promising that he would have offspring as numerous as dust particles on the earth, but nothing seemed to be happening and, as Abram pointed out, neither he nor Sarai were getting any younger. Sarai was so desperate for a child she suggested that Abram should sleep with her maid-servant Hagar to produce a family with her. And so Abram and Hagar had a son, which did not make for domestic bliss with Sarai. Hagar despised Sarai; Sarai ill-treated Hagar, and Abram was thoroughly miserable with them both.

Years pass, and when Abram is a very old man (99 years old) the Lord speaks to him again with the same promise. Abram's numbers are to greatly increase (what numbers?).

Abram will be the father of many nations. His name, Abram (which means *exalted father*) will from now on be Abraham (which means *father of many*). Abraham is lying face down on the ground, afraid to look at God, while God enlarges on his plans for Abraham: "I will make you very fruitful; I will make nations of you, and kings will come from you. I will establish my covenant as an everlasting covenant between me and you and your descendants after you for generations to come, to be your God and the God of your descendants after you. The whole land of Canaan, where you are now an alien, I will give you as an ever-lasting possession to you and your descendants after you; and I will be their God."

A sign of this covenant was to be circumcision. Sarai was also renamed:

she was to be called Sarah and she too was to be blessed. God said, "I will bless her and will surely give you a son by her. I will bless her so that she will be the mother of nations; kings of peoples will come from her." (Genesis 17:1-16)

Abraham, still lying flat on his face, laughed, but not with amusement. It was a cynical sort of laugh from a thoroughly frustrated and unhappy man. He said to himself, "Will a son be born to a man a hundred years old? Will Sarah bear a child at the age of ninety?" Abraham had not spoken aloud, and he had not addressed his question to God, but God heard him and repeated his promise: "Yes, but your wife Sarah will bear you a son and you will call him Isaac (which means, *'he laughs'*)."

God promised to bless Ishmael, Abraham's son by Hagar (Ishmael means *God hears*) but repeated the terms of his covenant to be established through the not-yet-conceived Isaac. So, as soon as God had finished speaking, on that very day, Abraham took his son Ishmael and all those born in his household or bought with his money, every male in his household, and circumcised them as God had told him to do. 'Abraham was ninety-nine years old when he was circumcised, and his son Ishmael was thirteen . . . And every male in Abraham's household, including those born in his household or bought from a foreigner, was circumcised with him.'

It was a hot day, and Abraham was sitting at the entrance to his tent under the shade of the great oaks of Mamre. Abraham was dozing at the time, but he had a feeling he was being watched. And so he was. He looked up and saw three men standing nearby. He hadn't heard them arrive, and there was no sign of any transport – no donkeys or camels or anything. Abraham got up, hurried to meet the men and bowed low. He begged them to stay and to rest in the shade of the oak tree, to allow their feet to be washed and to have something to eat. The men accepted Abraham's invitation.

Another strange thing about this story: There are three men, but Abraham addresses them as 'My Lord'. This is not an error in translation and it seems perfectly natural that the three should be addressed as one.

Abraham hurried into the tent to find Sarah to give her instructions about the meal, and what a meal! Servants were sent scurrying in all directions: bread was to be baked with the finest flour; a choice, tender calf was selected for preparation; curds and milk were to be brought. Abraham didn't sit down with the three men but stood near them under the tree while they ate. "Where is your wife Sarah?" they asked him. "There, in the tent," he replied.

Then Abraham is told that when the men (the Lord) pass by at the same time next year Sarah will have had a son.

'Now Sarah was listening at the entrance to the tent, which was behind him.' The promise was so preposterous that Sarah laughed to herself. She thought, "After I am worn out and my master is old, will I now have this pleasure?"

'Then the Lord said to Abraham, "Why did Sarah laugh and say, 'Will I really have a child, now that I am old?' Is anything too hard for the Lord? I will return to you at the appointed time next year and Sarah will have a son."

Sarah was afraid, so she lied and said, "I did not laugh." But the Lord said, "Yes, Sarah, you did laugh."

Quite a lot happens before we meet the three men again – Sodom and Gomorrah are destroyed because not one righteous man can be found in those hell-holes, and Lot has to be rescued, although his wife is turned into a pillar of salt for looking back. But (and we are now at chapter 21 of Genesis) ' . . . The Lord was gracious to Sarah as he had said, and the Lord did for Sarah what he had promised. Sarah became pregnant and bore a son to Abraham in his old age, at the very time God had promised him. Abraham gave the name Isaac to the son Sarah bore him. When his son Isaac was eight days old, Abraham circumcised him, as God commanded him. Abraham was a hundred years old when his son was born to him.

'Sarah said, "God has brought me laughter, and everyone who hears about this will laugh with me . . ." '

Poplar ~ *(Populus alba / P. tremuloides)*

Plant description

Ratcliffe says, 'Populus alba is a deciduous tree reaching a height of 30m with smooth, grey bark and white woolly shoots. The broadly ovate leaves are dark green above, white and woolly underneath. Poplars in general are fast growing and short-lived, producing softwood suitable only for the manufacture of paper pulp, matches and fruit crates. The white poplars are readily identifiable from among groups of mixed trees; and from a distance are easily picked out by the flashing white and grey leaves that move in the slightest breeze.'

Zohary describes a white poplar whose leaves are lobed, but which otherwise conforms to Ratcliffe's description. He further describes: 'The minute flowers, growing in loose, pendant catkins, appear before the leaves, each with a cup-shaped disk at its base and borne in the axil of a bract. The male flower has four or more stamens, the female a two- celled ovary with two or more stigmas. After pollination by the wind, the ovary becomes a capsule whose numerous small seeds are surrounded at the base by a tuft of long silky hairs which allow the seeds to be dispersed.'

Zohary also says that the white poplar is native to the Middle East, including Syria and Lebanon, and thrives along riverbanks and in damp places, where its whiteness stands out in the landscape against the surrounding verdure. He says, 'It was cultivated for its soft, workable timber, useful in making various agricultural and domestic tools, and for its straight trunk, excellent for roofing the houses in villages throughout the Middle East . . .'

The White Poplar is resistant to high winds and it throws suckers freely, so that it is useful for planting as a stabilizer for sandy soil near the sea.

Populus tremuloides – the Aspen – has a smooth silvery-green bark in its youth, and silver-grey velvety shoots. Leaves are almost circular and gently scalloped. This 'poplar' also likes damp places and often keeps company in woods with Birch and it is so prolific in suitable conditions that its suckers will form a thicket. The Aspen is widespread – from the Arctic to the Mediterranean and across Asia and is increasingly considered alongside '*Populus alba*'.

25

Plant lore

White poplar is mentioned at least twice in the mythology of Greece and Rome: Heracles (Hercules) killed Kakos in a mountain cave. The mountain was covered in poplars, and in his moment of triumph, Heracles plucked a branch from a tree and bound it round his brow. When he descended to the infernal regions, smoke from the eternal fires blackened the leaves, but his sweat blanched the under-surfaces – which is why poplar leaves are dark on one side and white on the other. Also, Pluto, who ruled the Underworld with his wife, Persephone (whose emblem is the Black Poplar), had a beautiful mistress, a nymph called Leuce. Sadly, unlike the gods, nymphs were merely mortal, so when Leuce died Pluto buried her in the Elysian Fields and planted a white poplar to mark her grave.

There is a small island called Leuce in the Black Sea. Poplars are said to have grown there at a time, but it is now treeless and has been used as a Romanian penal colony.

Uses in modern herbal medicine

Both bark and leaves of the White Poplar are used medicinally. An infusion can be used as a digestive restorative, as a relaxant for the intestinal tract when abdominal cramps and chronic diarrhoea present problems and as a diuretic. It can also be taken for the sort of headache which follows injudicious eating and that 'liverish' feeling. Poplar has been used to treat urethral discharges related to venereal disease, particularly in gonorrhoea.

SOME CRAFTY HUSBANDRY

God doesn't choose perfect people for his work, which is just as well since there aren't any perfect people. Even the great patriarchs had dubious backgrounds.

Jacob – who was to found a great dynasty, who was later to be called 'Israel', whose sons headed the twelve tribes of God's people – was involved in some pretty shady dealing in his early days.

First of all (Genesis 27), when Jacob's father, Isaac (son of Abraham) who was nearly sacrificed on Mount Moriah, was old and nearly blind,

Jacob cheated his twin brother, Esau out of the blessing due to the first-born (which meant that Jacob inherited everything when his father died).

Naturally enough, Esau held a grudge against Jacob, who had to flee for his life from his brother's rage. A very sad old Isaac, who loved both sons, told Jacob to go to Paddan Aram in the east and to look for Laban, an uncle on his mother's side who would give him work.

Here we must cut a very long story short: on his journey, Jacob falls in love with a beautiful girl called Rachel who is watering her father's flock at a well. By some wonderful chance, Rachel is Laban's younger daughter and she takes him home. Laban employs Jacob on a trial basis, and after a couple of months of earning nothing but his keep, Jacob is offered wages. He can choose what he wants, and so he chooses Rachel to be his wife. Laban has an elder daughter (who has been passed over before on account of her weak eyes), but, of course, Jacob is in love with Rachel and he agrees to work for seven years for Laban for Rachel.

After seven years, Jacob, who has been waiting for the day, reminds Laban of their deal, so Laban brings together all the people of the place and gives a great feast. 'But when evening came, (when, no doubt, nobody could see very well for one reason or another) he took his daughter Leah and gave her to Jacob . . .'

Not surprisingly, Jacob had a few things to say to Laban about the deception when he woke in the morning to find the considerably less appealing Leah in his bed. But, as Laban explained, it was not their custom to give the younger daughter before the elder. Jacob must make the best of it, but if he wanted Rachel as well then he must work another seven years for her. To give Laban his due, he only insisted on a week with Leah before Jacob was allowed to marry Rachel too, but nevertheless, Jacob had to work out the extra seven years.

Both Leah and Rachel produce sons for Jacob and after a time Jacob asks Laban to allow him to go back to his homeland, but Laban begs him to stay because all the time Jacob has been with him there has been blessing and increase on his house. "What shall I give you?" Laban asks. "Don't give me anything," Jacob replies. "But if you will do this one thing for me, I will go on tending your flocks and watching over them: let me go through all your flocks today and remove from them every speckled or spotted sheep, every dark-coloured lamb and every spotted or speckled goat. They will be my wages. And my honesty will testify for me in the future, whenever you check on the wages you have paid me. Any goat in my possession that is not speckled or spotted, or any lamb that is not dark-coloured will be considered stolen."

It seemed to Laban like an extremely good deal, and he agreed. That same day, Laban removed all the male goats that were streaked or spotted, and all the speckled or spotted female goats (all that had white on them) and all the dark-coloured lambs, and he placed them in his sons' care. 'Then he put a three-day journey between himself and Jacob. And Jacob continued to tend the rest of Laban's flocks.'

'Jacob, however, took fresh-cut branches from poplar, almond and plane trees and made white stripes on them by peeling the bark and exposing the white inner wood of the branches. Then he placed the peeled branches in all the watering troughs, so that they would be directly in front of the flocks when they came to drink. When the flocks were in heat and came to drink, they mated in front of the branches. And they bore young that were streaked or speckled or spotted. Jacob set apart the young of the flock by themselves but made the rest face the streaked and dark-coloured animals that belonged to Laban. Thus he made separate flocks for himself and did not put them with Laban's animals. Whenever the stronger females were in heat, Jacob would place the branches in the troughs in front of the animals so that they would mate near the branches, but if the animals were weak, he would not place them there. So the weak animals went to Laban and the strong ones to Jacob. In this way the man grew exceedingly prosperous and came to own large flocks and maid-servants and men-servants, and camels and donkeys.'

Laban's sons started a whispering campaign against Jacob, and 'Laban's attitude towards Jacob changed.' So Jacob sent for Leah and Rachel, reminded them of their father's earlier deceit and his present attitude and told them it was time to leave. They agreed, so: 'Then Jacob put his children and his wives on camels, and he drove all his livestock ahead of him, along with all the goods he had accumulated in Paddan Aram, to go to his father Isaac in the land of Canaan. However, 'When Laban had gone to shear his sheep, Rachel stole her father's household gods.

Moreover, Jacob deceived Laban, the Aramean by not telling him he was running away. So, he fled with all he had, and crossing the River (Euphrates), he headed for the hill country of Gilead.'

It took three days for Laban to find out what had happened, and he set out in hot pursuit. It was just as well for Jacob that God had appeared to Laban in a dream to tell him not to try to harm Jacob. As it was, Laban contented himself with an outraged tirade: "Why did you run off secretly and deceive me: why didn't you tell me, so that I could send you away with joy and singing to the music of tambourines and harps? You didn't even let me kiss my grandchildren and my daughters good-bye . . . But why did you steal my gods?"

Jacob invited Laban to search his tents for the gods, but Rachel had put them under her camel's saddle and she sat on it, so that nothing was found. In the end Jacob and Laban agreed a truce. Jacob set up a stone pillar, surrounded with small stones. Laban called it Jegar Sahadutha (in Aramaic it means *witness heap*) and Jacob called it Galeed (which in Hebrew means *camp*).

Laban said to Jacob, "This heap is a witness, and this pillar is a witness, that I will not go past this heap and pillar to my side to harm you and that you will not go past this heap and pillar to my side to harm me."

Laban swore an oath in the name of Abraham and of his gods and Jacob took an oath in the name of his father, Isaac. He offered sacrifice there in the hill country and invited everyone to a meal.

Early the next morning, Laban kissed his grandchildren and his daughters and blessed them. Then he left and returned home.

Wheat ~ (*Triticum durum*)

Plant description

Wheat is a member of the Grass family derived from a perennial grass native to the Middle East. Zohary says, 'Its species are all annual, with erect culms ending in an ear of spikelets along the central axis (rhachis). Each spikelet has three to seven flowers, of which only a few produce grains. These, the fruit of the wheat, contain a single seed with a minute embryo and a large body of endosperm storing about seventy per cent of starch and about ten per cent of proteins. The coats, or outer layers of the seeds, are bran, which is most nutritive for cattle and poultry.'

Zohary continues: 'The main field crop of biblical times was wheat. The fields were not irrigated and were fully dependent upon the highly unstable annual rainfall, which was sometimes so scanty that the fields 'did not yield their crops.' **Disastrous famine years are frequently mentioned in the Bible, which speaks of Egypt as a wheatland with abundant water for irrigation, a granary for its famine-afflicted neighbours.**

'There were two species abundantly cultivated in Israel and the neighbouring countries, both tetraploid, one the so-called durum wheat (*T. durum* – hard wheat) and the other 'emmer' (*T. dicoccum*). The former is still, as it was in the time of the Bible, the dominant field crop grown commonly for bread in the warm-temperate countries. Its grains are free (not hulled), hard, rich in gluten and supply excellent flour. It is sown before or after the early rains and harvested in June or July . . .'

Plant lore

King Solomon had a rather good *quid pro quo* with Hiram, king of Tyre while he (Solomon) was building the Temple: Hiram supplied all the cedar and pine logs, his men hauling them down from Lebanon to the sea and then floating them in rafts to a place chosen by Solomon. In return for materials and labour, Hiram received vast amounts of wheat and pressed olive oil. 'The Lord gave Solomon wisdom, just as he had promised him. There were peaceful relations between Hiram and Solomon, and the two of them made a treaty.' (I Kings 5)

And back in Deuteronomy, chapter 8, God instructs the Israelites not to forget him: 'Observe the commands of the Lord your God, walking in his ways and revering him. For the Lord your God is bringing you into a good land – a land with streams and pools of water, with springs flowing in the valleys and hills; **a land with wheat and barley, vines and fig trees, pomegranates, olive oil and honey;** a land where bread will not be scarce and you will lack nothing; a land where rocks are iron and you can dig copper out of the hills.'

The Israelites enjoyed 'the seven species with which the land was blessed' but forgot their part of the bargain and got into terrible trouble.

Uses in modern herbal medicine

Wheat has become much more sophisticated recently. It has always been used as a poultice (breadcrumbs added to boiling water, drained and applied to painful swellings), but now the wheat germ, rich in vitamins, is taken as a health food supplement and wheat germ oil, particularly rich in vitamin E, is taken in capsule form to improve circulation.

Gluten, the protein in wheat, may cause allergies in some people. These allergies (or hypersensitivities) range widely from mild abdominal discomfort to coeliac disease, and those suffering from 'gluten-induced enteropathy' must keep to a gluten-free (wheat and rye-free) diet.

JOSEPH AND HIS RICHLY ORNAMENTED ROBE
(More usually known as his coat of many colours)

Joseph's half-brothers hated him, which is hardly surprising because – not to put too fine a point upon it – he was a brat. He told tales about his elder brothers to his father, not the most endearing trait in a teenager, and when he had dreams about his brothers bowing down to him (sheaves and sun and moon and stars) he was fool enough to boast about his dreams.

Jacob was a bit foolish about the boy too, giving him a richly ornamented robe to wear because Joseph was his favourite son, born in his old age. Not a wise thing for a father to do. The elder sons probably longed to give Joseph a good beating, but didn't dare to touch him while their father was around.

However, in Genesis, chapter 37, Joseph gets his comeuppance. He (Joseph) is sent to take provisions to his brothers who are looking after their father's flocks near Shechem. 'So Joseph went in search of his brothers, but they saw him coming and plotted to kill him and to throw him into a nearby cistern (an underground reservoir for rain water). They planned to say that a ferocious animal had killed him, but one of the brothers, Reuben, persuaded them not to kill Joseph, just to throw him into a cistern – because Reuben meant to rescue Joseph and take him home to his father.'

So the brothers stripped Joseph of his splendid robe and threw him into the cistern and, quite pleased with themselves at this, sat down to a meal. No doubt Joseph was being pretty vocal while this was going on, howling from the depths of the cistern, (which was dry because there had been no rain), and no doubt his brothers were enjoying his discomfort and cries of outrage.

While the brothers were eating their meal, they saw a caravan of Ishmaelites coming from Gilead on their way to Egypt, the camels loaded with spices, balm and myrrh. One of them, Judah, had a bright idea; he said to the others: "What will we gain if we kill our brother and cover up his blood? Come, let's sell him to the Ishmaelites and not lay our hands on him; after all, he is our brother, our own flesh and blood."

So the boys pulled Joseph out of the cistern and sold him to the Ishmaelites. Then they dipped Joseph's fine robe in goat's blood and took it back to their father, who naturally assumed his son had been eaten by some animal, and he nearly died of grief.

In Egypt, Joseph was sold on – to Potiphar, the captain of Pharaoh's guard, who was so pleased with his new acquisition that he put him in charge of his household. 'From the time he put him in charge of his household and of all that he owned, the Lord blessed the household of the Egyptian because of Joseph. The blessing of the Lord was upon everything Potiphar had, both in the house and in the field. So he left in Joseph's care everything he had; with Joseph in charge, he did not concern himself with anything except the food he ate.' (Genesis 39:1-8)

Wonderful. But trouble is looming in the shape of Potiphar's wife who is probably bored with her husband away such a lot, and we are told that Joseph is a handsome young man who is about the place all the time. She invites (orders) Joseph to "Come to bed with me!" Joseph declines the offer every time it is made on the grounds that he is loyal to his master, and she is so furious that she makes the age-old accusation of attempted rape and Joseph finds himself in prison. But even in prison ' . . . the Lord was with him; he showed him kindness and granted him favour in the eyes of the prison warder. So the warder put Joseph in charge of all those held in the prison, and he was made responsible for all that was done there. The warder paid no attention to anything under Joseph's care, because the Lord was with Joseph and he gave him success in whatever he did.'

A couple of years passed and Pharaoh began to have strange dreams. First, Pharaoh saw seven sleek, fat cows grazing by the Nile; these were followed by seven other cows, ugly and gaunt. The ugly gaunt cows ate the sleek fat cows. In his second dream, Pharaoh saw seven ears of good healthy corn, growing on a single stalk. After them, seven others sprouted, but they were thin and scorched by the east wind. The thin ears of corn swallowed up the healthy, full ears. Pharaoh sent for all the magicians and wise men in Egypt, but no-one could interpret his dreams. Then Pharaoh's cup-bearer (who had spent some time in prison with Joseph) told the king that Joseph could interpret dreams, and he was sent for. Joseph listened carefully, and then told Pharaoh that there would be seven years of great abundance in Egypt, followed by seven years of terrible famine. Joseph was immediately reinstated and put in charge of the whole land. He had as much authority as the king himself, wearing Pharaoh's ring, dressing in fine linen, riding in a chariot and acquiring a wife.

'Joseph was thirty years old when he entered the service of Pharaoh, king of Egypt. And Joseph went out from Pharaoh's presence and travelled throughout Egypt. During the seven years of abundance the land produced plentifully. Joseph collected all the food produced in those seven years of abundance in Egypt and stored it in the cities. In each city he put the food grown in the fields surrounding it . . . Joseph stored up huge quantities of grain, like the sand of the sea; it was so much that he stopped keeping records because it was beyond measure.'

' . . . The seven years of abundance in Egypt came to an end, and the seven years of famine began, just as Joseph had said. There was famine in all the other lands, but in the whole land of Egypt there was food . . . When the famine had spread over the whole country, Joseph opened the storehouses and sold grain to the Egyptians, for the famine was severe throughout Egypt. And all the countries came to Egypt to buy grain from Joseph, because the famine was severe in all the world. (To be continued . . .)

Pistachio ~ (*Pistacia vera*)

Plant description

Zohary says, 'The pistachio is a small deciduous tree whose trunk has a multitude of branches and whose leaves consist of two or three pairs of rather large, ovate leaflets with minute unisexual flowers, male and female on different trees. The fruits are one-seeded nuts with a hard shell which splits along a lateral suture. The tasty, fatty kernel is about 1cm long.

'The pistachio is a steppe tree, growing wild in semi-arid countries of southwest Asia amid a steppe-like dwarf shrubbery. It was probably introduced into Israel from Syria or directly from Persia, along with other cultivated plants.'

The pistachio belongs to the Anacardiacae family, native to western Asia and now much cultivated in southern Europe. The edible kernel of the fruit drupe is a distinctive pale green in colour The genus *Pistacia* includes the mastic tree (*P. lentiscus*) and the turpentine tree (*P. terebinthus*).

Plant lore

The pistachio tree itself is not mentioned in the Bible. Zohary says, 'Pistachio nuts (*botnim*) are only mentioned once in the Bible, in a list of appropriate gifts for an esteemed man, and so they must have been considered one of the Land's most delicious fruits. The place name Betonim (Joshua 13:26), in the district of the tribe of Gad in southern Transjordan, an area suited to the pistachio, is probably derived from *botnim*. These two passages and a reference in the Talmud make it clear that the tree has long been cultivated in Israel; a pistachio nut has in fact been found in the late Neolithic stratum in Greece.'

Uses in modern herbal medicine

Like most other nuts, the Pistachio is rich in fat, protein, vitamins and trace elements. Like most other nuts they are nutritious and sustaining and they are used widely in confectionary and ice cream (as well as giving their name to the lovely pale green colour beloved of those who dye fashion fabrics). I have been unable to confirm a specific use in modern herbal medicine, but Pistachio nuts are said to have been used medicinally in East India.

Pistacia lentiscus, a close relation of *Pistacia vera*, is the Mastic, a small tree, indigenous to Mediterranean countries. The Mastic yields an oily resin which hardens on contact with air, used now to produce varnish and waterproof fillers and sealants in the building industry. However, in the past this resin was used in a surgical varnish as a temporary filling for carious teeth and for chewing in a 'gum' to sweeten the breath.

JOSEPH AND HIS RICHLY ORNAMENTED ROBE
(Continued)

. . . Meanwhile, Jacob and his family, back in Canaan, heard that there was grain to be had in Egypt. He said to his sons, who were obviously short on ideas about how to cope with the famine there, "I have heard that there is grain to be had in Egypt. Don't just stand there looking at each other. Go and get some, or we shall all die."

And so ten of Joseph's brothers went to buy grain from Egypt, but they didn't take Benjamin, the very youngest, who had been a baby when Joseph 'disappeared' all those years ago. Benjamin was the son of Jacob's old age and he wouldn't let the boy out of his sight. (Benjamin was Joseph's full brother – all the others had different mothers.)

Joseph had really risen to the heights because of what he had done for Egypt. He was now governor of the whole land, the one who had control over the stores of grain. So when Joseph's brothers arrived and saw him, they bowed down to him.

Joseph recognised them, but they didn't recognise him. He embarked on a pretence, speaking harshly to them. "Where do you come from?" he snapped. "From Canaan, to buy food," they answered. "You are spies!" he accused them, and in their fear they blurted out about their old father and their youngest brother back home. So, his father was still alive; that was a huge relief. But Joseph hadn't finished with them yet; not by a long way. He insisted that one of the brothers should go home to fetch Benjamin, and he threw the others into prison for three days.

When Joseph had the sorry bunch brought before him again, he repeated his demand that one of them should go and fetch Benjamin. They were to take grain back to their starving households, but one must stay behind as hostage until they returned with Benjamin.

They talked among themselves. They said: "Surely we are being punished for our treatment of our brother Joseph. He pleaded for his life, but we wouldn't listen." Reuben, the one who had been against the idea of harming Joseph at the time, was distressed. "Now it's our turn to suffer," he said. "And parting with Benjamin will kill our father."

Joseph understood every word, of course, and he had to turn away from them so that they couldn't see his tears, but he managed to continue the charade. He had Simeon taken from the group, bound and taken away to prison while they could only stand and watch. Joseph gave orders for their bags to be filled with grain (and for each brother's silver to be put back in his sack secretly). Then they loaded up their donkeys with provisions for the journey and left.

When they stopped for the night, one of the brothers opened his sack to get some feed for his donkey, and he saw his silver in the mouth of his sack. He showed it to the others, who were all even more terrified; their hearts sank, they trembled and said, "What is this that God has done to us?"

'When they came to their father Jacob in the land of Canaan, they told him all that had happened to them. They said, "The man who is lord over the land spoke harshly to us and treated us as though we were spying on the land. But we said to him, "We are honest men, we are not spies. We were twelve brothers, sons of one father. One is no more, and the youngest is now with our father in Canaan.

' "Then the man who is lord over the land said to us, 'This is how I will know whether you are honest men: Leave one of your brothers here with me, and take food for your starving households and go. But bring your youngest brother to me so I will know that you are not spies but honest men. Then I will give your brother back to you and you can trade in the land." ' (Genesis 42:29-34)

As they were emptying their sacks, there in each man's sack was his pouch of silver! When they and their father saw the money pouches, they were frightened. Their father Jacob said to them, "You have deprived me of my children. Joseph is no more and Simeon is no more, and now you want to take Benjamin. Everything is against me."

Reuben offered to go. He even offered his own sons to be put to death if he didn't return with Benjamin, but Jacob refused.

However, when the famine was unrelenting, when all the grain had gone and they were starving, Jacob finally agreed. **"If it must be so, then do this: Put some of the best products of the land in your bags and take them down to the man as a gift – a little balm, a little honey, some spices and myrrh, some pistachio nuts and almonds. Take double the amount of silver with you, for you must return the silver that was put back into the mouths of your sacks. Perhaps it was a mistake.**

"Take your brother also and go to the man at once. And may God Almighty grant you mercy before the man so that he will let your other brother and Benjamin come back with you. As for me, if I am bereaved, I am bereaved."

'So the brothers took the gifts and double the amount of silver, and Benjamin also. They hurried down to Egypt and presented themselves to Joseph.

'When Joseph saw Benjamin with them, he said to the steward of his house, "Take these men to my house, slaughter an animal and prepare dinner; they are to eat with me at noon." ' (Genesis 43:11–16)

The brothers were very frightened. Why were they invited to the Egyptian lord's house? What was he going to do to them? Before they went into the house they spoke to the head steward, telling him of what had happened on their previous visit. He reassured them that everything was all right, and he brought their brother Simeon out to join them. The steward offered them great hospitality – like honoured guests. He gave them water to wash and provided fodder for their donkeys. In the meantime, the brothers prepared the gifts they had brought.

When Joseph came in they presented him with their gifts and bowed low before him. When Joseph saw Benjamin, the son of his own mother, he was so overcome that he had to go to his private room to weep. When he had recovered, Joseph returned and ordered the food to be served, and Benjamin's portion was five times the size of anyone else's. 'So they feasted and drank freely with him.'

But Joseph still plays with his brothers. He orders his steward to fill the men's sacks to the top, to put each man's silver in the mouth of his sack again, plus, this time, to put his own silver cup in the mouth of Benjamin's sack. Then, before the men have gone far on their journey home, the steward comes racing after them and accuses them of theft. The sacks are opened, the silver is found and they are all hauled back to the city. There is no way of proving their innocence: all the terrified brothers can do is to offer themselves as slaves.

Suddenly, Joseph has had enough of games. He can no longer control himself in front of his attendants and dismisses them. 'So there was no-one with Joseph when he made himself known to his brothers. And he wept so loudly that the Egyptians heard him, and Pharaoh's household heard about it.'

We must leave Joseph and his brothers to their reunion: it is too intimate and emotional for our eyes. We only know that he was generous in his forgiveness and gave all credit to God. When Pharaoh heard, he said to Joseph, "Tell your brothers, 'Do this: Load your animals and return to the land of Canaan, and bring your father and your families back to me. I will give you the best of the land of Egypt and you can enjoy the fat of the land . . . Never mind about your belongings, because the best of all Egypt will be yours." '

And so it was. God spoke to old Jacob in a vision. He said, "I am God . . . do not be afraid to go down to Egypt, for I will make you into a great nation." And they did become a great nation, founding the twelve tribes of Israel.

Note: Jacob was called 'Israel' which means '*he struggles with God*' after his all-night struggle with the 'man' who would not tell Jacob his name, but gave him a blessing. Jacob called the place 'Peniel' – which means '*face of God*' because, he said, "It is because I saw God face to face, and yet my life was spared." (Genesis 32:22-32)

Senna ~ (*Cassia senna*)

Plant description

Zohary says, 'The senna bush is a shrub up to 1m high. The stems and branches are richly beset with pinnate leaves, made up of three to seven oblong, acute leaflets. In the axils of the upper leaves the plant develops racemes of large yellow flowers, which yield straight or slightly curved, many-seeded pods.

'A tropical plant requiring warmth, it grows in stony wadis both in the Sinai and in southern Israel. It is known medically as a stimulant and purgative, under the name *folia sennae*.'

Plant lore

There seems to have been a great deal of argument as to whether the Burning Bush of Moses (given the name '*sneh*' in the original Hebrew) was senna – whose large abundant flowers are striped red – or a bramble '*Rubus sanguineus*', which was a flowering currant with blood-coloured blossom. Some think it was a species of hawthorn with crimson flowers resembling flames; others that it might have been an acacia bush infested with the crimson-coloured mistletoe (*Loranthus acaciae*). For myself, I am happy to leave the botanical scholars discussing these possibilities and to go on, just accepting the mystery and the story of a man who had to cross a desert before arriving at Horeb, the mountain of God

I can find no direct reference to senna in poetry or literature, but as I write it is the first week in Lent. A week ago today, on Ash Wednesday, we were reminded that we are dust and that to dust we shall return. We embarked upon our Lenten journey; we made our gestures of self denial, we committed ourselves to fasting, to prayer and to almsgiving. During Lent we use King David's great psalm of penitence (Psalm 51). In the KJAV it says, **'Purge me with hyssop, and I shall be clean: wash me, and I shall be whiter than snow . . .'** We shall be meeting hyssop later in another context, but senna too is a purgative, a 'cleansing agent'.

Uses in modern herbal medicine

Senna is a strong stimulant laxative which should not be taken during pregnancy, while breastfeeding, or in conditions of inflammatory bowel disorders. It is also contra-indicated in children. Senna should not be taken for more than ten days at a time since prolonged use can cause a wide range of health problems.

Chevallier says of 'Indications for use': 'Senna's sureness of action as a laxative has made it the most frequently used herbal medicine for constipation, and it is prescribed throughout the world for this purpose. Its first documented use was by Arabian physicians in the 9th century, though its use as a medicine is ancient.

'Both leaf and fruit of Senna (its Arabic name) are highly effective in relieving *short term* constipation where this is due to reduced colonic muscle tone or excessively dry stools. However, its use should be avoided where constipation results from excessive muscle tone, e.g. in cases of irritable bowel. As long term use is potentially harmful, every effort should be made to improve bowel regularity in other ways whilst taking Senna, e.g. by dietary means – increased intake of whole grains, fresh vegetables, seeds such as linseed, dried fruit, water etc. and with regular exercise . . .

'As a cathartic, Senna is liable to cause griping and colicky pains if taken alone, and it is best taken with aromatic or carminative herbs, which relax the intestinal muscles. Ginger, Cinnamon, Nutmeg and Cloves are good examples.

'Senna provides effective though temporary relief for painful haemorrhoids and anal fissure when these are exacerbated by dry, abrasive stools, and in Middle Eastern and Ayurvedic medicine, both leaf and fruit are used for a variety of problems including skin disorders, jaundice, bronchitis and fevers.'

THE BURNING BUSH

We ended the Book of Genesis on a high note. Jacob died happy and full of years; his sons and their families were well established in Egypt, respected, honoured and settled. Joseph's name was renowned in the land as the one who saved the nation from great hardship in a time of famine.

But many years have passed and the Israelites have more than fulfilled God's instruction to 'be fruitful and multiply'. From a family of about seventy descendants of Jacob they now number a couple of million. 'The land was filled with them.' The original family have all died, and so has the old benign and grateful Pharaoh. There is a new ruler who doesn't know or care about Joseph and his family. "Look,' he says to his people, "The Israelites have become much too numerous for us. Come, we must deal shrewdly with them or they will become even more numerous and, if war breaks out, will join our enemies, fight against us and leave the country." See how fear breeds hatred; and it is not difficult to find parallels in our own time.

Hebrew midwives are instructed to kill boys at birth but, courageously, they find excuses not to do so. Then Pharaoh orders the Egyptians to take every new-born boy and throw him into the Nile.

A man and woman (named elsewhere in 'the annals' but not here in Exodus), both from priestly families, have a son. The mother manages to hide the baby for three months, but then is forced to take an enormous risk. She gets a papyrus basket, coats it with tar and pitch, lays her son in it and places it among the reeds by the river bank. Her daughter is posted, at a distance, to see what will happen and to report back.

Enter Pharaoh's daughter with her retinue, down to the Nile to bathe. She sees the basket among the reeds and sends her slave girl to retrieve it. The baby in the basket is crying and she feels sorry for it. "This is one of the Hebrew babies," she says.

The baby's sister comes nearer and asks Pharaoh's daughter if she would like her to get one of the Hebrew women to nurse the child for her, and Pharaoh's daughter say, "Yes, go." So the girl goes and brings her mother, who not only has her son back but is paid for looking after him.

When the child is old enough, the mother takes him to Pharaoh's daughter, who takes him as her son. She names him Moses, saying, "I drew him out of the water."

And so Moses is brought up as an Egyptian at the Egyptian court, the adopted son of an Egyptian princess. No doubt it is a life of luxury and security, but he never loses sight of his roots – which is good, and not so good. 'One day, after Moses had grown up, he went out to where his own people were and watched them at their hard labour. He saw an Egyptian beating a Hebrew, one of his own people.'

Moses glances this way and that and, thinking there is no-one to see him, kills the Egyptian and hides him in the sand. But, of course, he has been seen and he has to flee to save his own life.

Moses is still dressed as an Egyptian when he sits down by a well in Midian. While he sits there, no doubt pondering his uncertain future, the seven daughters of the priest of Midian come along to draw water to fill the troughs to water their father's flock. Some rough shepherds drive them away, but Moses, probably an impressive figure in his exotic clothes, drives them away and waters the girls' sheep for them. Galant too. Good manners learnt at court stood him in good stead that day.

The girls are grateful, they say their thank-you's and return home to their father, who wants to know why they are back so much earlier than usual. When they tell him about the Egyptian who rescued them from the uncouth shepherds, who drew water for them and who watered the flock, their father sends them back straight away to bring Moses home to dinner.

Moses stays for much more than dinner; he marries Zipporah, one of the daughters of the priest of Midian and they have a son whom Moses names Gershom, "Because," he says, "I am an alien in a foreign land."

'Now Moses was tending the flock of Jethro his father-in-law, the priest of Midian, and he led the flock to the far side of the desert and came to Horeb, the mountain of God. There the angel of the Lord appeared to him in flames of fire from within a bush. Moses saw that though the bush was on fire it did not burn up. So Moses thought, "I will go over and see this strange sight – why the bush does not burn up." ' (Exodus 3:1-3)

Having got Moses attention, God gets straight to the point: "Do not come any closer," God says. "Take off your sandals, for the place where you are standing is holy ground."

Then God identifies himself: "I am the God of your father, the God of Abraham, the God of Isaac and the God of Jacob." At this, Moses hides his face, because he is afraid to look at God.

God says that he has seen the misery of the Israelites in slavery, has heard them crying out, is concerned about their suffering. He is going to rescue them, bring them out of Egypt into a land flowing with milk and honey. (Watch out Moses, here comes the punch- line!) God says, "So now, go. I am sending you to Pharaoh to bring my people the Israelites out of Egypt."

Moses, of course, is horrified and begins to argue, but God says he is not to worry, he will be with Moses and, when Moses has accomplished his little task, he and the Israelites will worship God on Mount Horeb.

Playing for time, Moses says, "Suppose I go to the Israelites and say to them, 'The God of your fathers has sent me to you,' and they ask me, 'What is his name?' Then what shall I tell them?" God said to Moses, "I Am Who I Am. This is what you are to say to the Israelites: 'I Am has sent me to you.'"

This does not satisfy Moses. He says, "What if they do not believe me or listen to me and say, "The Lord did not appear to you?"

So God shows Moses two miraculous signs: first his staff becomes a snake when it is thrown to the ground, and it reverts to being a staff again when Moses catches it by the tail. If he didn't like that sign (and he most assuredly did not), he is not likely to appreciate the second one either: God asks him to put his hand inside his cloak, and when he takes it out it is covered in the lesions of leprosy, much more terrifying even than the snake. But when God asks him to put his hand again inside his cloak and take it out again, his hand is restored to normal. God also tells Moses how to change the water of the Nile into blood when it is poured on the dry ground.

Moses is really in difficulties now. He tries pleading inadequacy in speech; he has never been eloquent, always slow of tongue (he says). You can almost hear God sigh; he says to Moses, "Who gave man his mouth? Who makes him deaf or mute? Who gives him sight or makes him blind? Is it not I, the Lord? Now go; I will help you to speak and teach you what to say."

Moses has his back against a wall. He can find no more excuses. He can only whimper, "O Lord, please send someone else to do it."

God has had enough. It is time to cut across all this nonsense. He says Aaron, Moses' brother, can do the speaking. God says, "He will speak to the people for you and it will be as if he were your mouth and as if you were God to him."

And so, Moses goes back to Jethro, his father-in-law, and asks for release to go back to Egypt, and Jethro sends him off with his blessing.

'So Moses took his wife and sons, put them on a donkey and started back to Egypt. And he took the staff of God in his hand.' (Exodus 4:20)

Syrian Hyssop ~ (*Origanum syriacum*)

Plant description

Zohary describes the Syrian hyssop as '. . . a stout, many-stemmed, hairy grey shrub about 70cm tall, with ovate to elliptical leaves, opposite and entire. The white, rather small flowers are grouped in dense spikes on the upper part of the branches. The flowers, which appear in midsummer, are subtended by woolly bracts as long as the calyx, made up of a flattened hairy lip. The corolla, from which the four stamens are exserted, is two-lipped. The fruit is a minute nutlet enclosed in the calyx and is dispersed by the wind.'

The Syrian hyssop is a member of the Marjoram family of plants, and its short twigs, bound together, lend themselves to use as small brushes for applying blood or water to persons or buildings in religious rituals.

The Syrian hyssop may not be the most beautiful plant in the world (unlike the European hyssop – *Hyssopus officinalis* – which is an aromatic, attractive perennial border plant with a long flowering season), but it will grow in harsh conditions, on stony ground, and it can be used as a spice in both tea and cooked food.

Plant lore

The first reference to hyssop in the Bible is in the Book of Exodus, and we shall be looking at that story in a moment.

In the Book of Leviticus (Chapter 14) there is the regulation on cleansing from infectious skin diseases (including leprosy). In preparation for the cleansing rituals, two live, clean birds were taken, one was killed, the other dipped into the blood of the dead bird, **together with cedar wood, scarlet yarn and hyssop.** The person with the skin infection was then sprinkled with the blood of the dead bird seven times, then the live bird was released.

In the Book of Numbers (Chapter 19) we find similar preparation of water for ritual cleansing: A perfect red heifer is sacrificed and burned. The priest takes **cedar wood, hyssop and scarlet wool** and throws them on to the burning heifer . . . the ashes are gathered up, taken to a place that is ceremonially clean outside the camp and kept for purification purposes when someone has become unclean.

In I Kings, chapter 4 we read: 'God gave Solomon wisdom and very great insight, and a breadth of understanding as measureless as the sand on the seashore. Solomon's wisdom was greater than the wisdom of all the men of Egypt. He was wiser than any other man, including Ethan the Ezrathite – wiser than Heman, Calcol and Darda, the sons of Mahol. And his fame spread to all the surrounding nations. He spoke three thousand proverbs and his songs numbered a thousand and five. **He described plant life, from the cedar of Lebanon to the hyssop that grows out of walls.** He also taught about animals and birds, reptiles and fish. Men of all nations came to listen to Solomon's wisdom, sent by all the kings of the world, who had heard of his wisdom.'

In Psalm 51:7 we find King David pleading for God's cleansing after he had sinned: **'Cleanse me with hyssop, and I shall be clean; wash me, and I shall be whiter than snow.'**

In the New Testament, (John 19:28-30) Jesus speaks from the Cross: 'Later, knowing that all was now completed, and so that the Scripture would be fulfilled, Jesus said, "I am thirsty." **A jar of wine vinegar was there, so they soaked a sponge in it, put the sponge on a stalk of the hyssop plant, and lifted it to Jesus' lips.** When he had received the drink, Jesus said, "It is finished." With that, he bowed his head and gave up his spirit.'

Uses in modern herbal medicine
Hyssop has long been used for coughs, colds, in febrile influenza, and for bronchitis – either in syrup form or in an infusion.

As a lotion, hyssop can be used for mild burns (where the skin is unbroken), bruises, and skin irritations. Towelling can be dipped into the hyssop lotion, wrung out, and used as a hot (not too hot) poultice.

Hyssop contains a camphoraceous oil, made into a bath oil for use at the end of a tiring day, but essential oil of hyssop should be treated with caution as it has been blamed for causing epileptic fits. Conversely, combined in an infusion with Betony, it has been used to treat epilepsy

Hyssop is one of the ingredients of the liqueur, Chartreuse, which may or may not be considered medicinal!

THE GREAT ESCAPE

In the last chapter we left Moses and his family making their way back to Egypt. On arrival, Moses and Aaron met all the elders of the Israelites and told them everything God had said to Moses: 'He also performed the signs before the people and they believed. And when they heard that the Lord was concerned about them and had seen their misery, they bowed down and worshipped.'

That was the first small hurdle negotiated, but, of course, when the pair visited Pharaoh and said, with great civility, that the God of Israel has asked for his people to be released so that they could hold a festival to him in the desert, Pharaoh laughed at them. "Who is this 'Lord' that I should obey him and let Israel go?" he said. "I do not know this Lord, and I will not let Israel go."

That was a predictable reaction, and so, probably, was his next piece of nastiness. 'That same day Pharaoh gave this order to the slave drivers and foremen in charge of the people: "You are no longer to supply the people with straw for making bricks as before; don't reduce the quota. They are lazy; that is why they are crying out, 'Let us go and sacrifice to our God.' Make the work harder for them so that they keep working and pay no attention to their lies." '

No prizes for guessing who got the blame! Moses was about to find out what life was going to be like for the next four decades with the Israelites, who drove him mad with their constant grumbling. Moses had a word with God, who told him to go back to the Israelites with promises: "I am the Lord, and I will bring you out from under the yoke of the Egyptians. I will free you from being slaves to them, and I will redeem you with an outstretched arm and with mighty acts of judgement. I will take you as my own people, and I will be your God . . ."

If the Israelites expected this to happen immediately, they must have been sorely disappointed. Pharaoh had no intention of letting his entire workforce leave the country. Even through the ten plagues that God sent on Egypt (which affected everyone except the Israelites), Pharaoh 'hardened his heart', which meant that he got more and more angry and more and more determined to keep the Israelites in slavery.

Plague after plague, Moses went back to Pharaoh to bargain for release: plagues of drinking water turned to blood; the land covered with frogs, with gnats, with flies; plagues that killed all the livestock; of boils, hail, locusts and darkness; and each time Pharaoh hardened his heart and would not let them go. Finally there was the most terrible plague of all.

Moses told Pharaoh, "This is what the Lord says: 'About midnight I will go throughout Egypt. Every first born son in Egypt will die, from the first born son of Pharaoh, who sits on the throne, to the first born son of the slave girl, who is at her hand-mill, and all the first born of the cattle as well. There will be loud wailing throughout Egypt – worse than there has ever been or ever will be again. But among the Israelites not a dog will bark at any man or animal.' Then you will know that the Lord makes a distinction between Egypt and Israel . . .'" Then Moses, hot with anger, left Pharaoh.' (Exodus 11)

God gave Moses precise instructions about that first Passover. Each family was to take a small lamb (or share with their neighbours). Blood from the lamb was to be daubed on the side-posts of their homes and on the tops of the door-frames. The meat itself was to be roasted over a fire and served with bitter herbs and bread made without yeast. None must be left. The meal was to be eaten with everyone in a state of readiness for flight. God said . . . "This is how you are to eat it: with your cloak tucked into your belt, your sandals on your feet and your staff in your hand. Eat it in haste; it is the Lord's Passover."

Moses summoned all the elders of Israel and said to them, **"Go at once and select the animals for your families and slaughter the Passover lamb. Take a bunch of hyssop, dip it into the blood in the basin and put some of the blood on the top and on both sides of the door-frame. Not one of you shall go out of the door of his house until morning. When the Lord goes through the land to strike the Egyptians, he will see the blood on the top and sides of the door and will pass over that doorway, and he will not permit the destroyer to enter your house and strike you down."**

For once, the Israelites obeyed Moses and it was done to the letter. 'At midnight, the Lord struck down all the first born in Egypt, from the first born of Pharaoh, who sat on the throne, to the first born of the prisoner, who was in the dungeon, and the first born of all the livestock as well. Pharaoh and all his officials and all the Egyptians got up during the night, and there was a loud wailing in Egypt, for there was not one house without someone dead.'

Pharaoh called for Moses and Aaron in the middle of the night. "Up!" he said. "Leave my people, you and the Israelites! Go, worship the Lord as you have requested. Take your flocks and herds . . . Go!"

And so they went, but Pharaoh had second thoughts yet again: "What have we done?" he said. "We have let the Israelites go and have lost their services!" So he had his chariot made ready and he took his army with him in pursuit. When the Israelites saw them coming they were terrified. They did what they always did when they were caught in a bad situation, they complained bitterly to Moses, saying that they would have been better off staying in Egypt. Moses (to whom God had told his plan in advance) was able to reassure them: the Israelites were not to worry, God was about to change the situation to great advantage . . . 'Then the angel of God, who had been travelling in front of Israel's army, withdrew and went behind them. The pillar of cloud also moved from in front and stood behind them, coming between the armies of Egypt and Israel. Throughout the night the cloud brought darkness to the one side and light to the other; so neither went near the other all night long.

'Then Moses stretched out his hand over the sea, and all that night the Lord drove the sea back with a strong east wind and turned it into dry land. The waters were divided, and the Israelites went through the sea on dry ground, with a wall of water on their right and on their left.

'The Egyptians pursued them, and all Pharaoh's horses and chariots and horsemen followed them into the sea. During the last watch of the night the Lord looked down from the pillar of fire and cloud at the Egyptian army and threw it into confusion. He made the wheels of their chariots come off so that they had difficulty driving. And the Egyptians said, "Let's get away from the Israelites! The Lord is fighting for them against Egypt!"

Too late! 'Then the Lord said to Moses, "Stretch out your hand over the sea so that the waters may flow back over the Egyptians and their chariots and horsemen." So Moses stretched out his hand over the sea, and at daybreak the sea went back to its place. The Egyptians were fleeing towards it, and the Lord swept them into the sea. The water flowed back and covered the chariots and horsemen – the entire army of Pharaoh that had followed the Israelites into the sea. Not one of them survived.

'But the Israelites went through the sea on dry ground, with a wall of water on their right and on their left. That day the Lord saved Israel from the hands of the Egyptians . . . And when the Israelites saw the great power the Lord displayed against the Egyptians, the people feared the Lord and put their trust in him and in Moses his servant.' (Exodus, chapters 12, 13 and 14)

Coriander ~ (*Coriandrum sativum*)

Plant description

Coriander is a hardy annual herb, a member of the Carrot family, and it is aromatic in all its parts. Slender in form, it grows to a height of 0.6m. Its lower leaves are fan-shaped, while those above are delicate and feathery. In July, pale mauve flowerets lie in flat clusters and its tiny round seeds ripen in late summer. Fine upper leaves are used for flavouring in soups and green salads; seeds are ground and used as a spicy condiment.

Coriander has been known in Mediterranean countries and the Middle East for several thousand years, but it is now used the world over for both culinary and medicinal purposes.

Plant lore

There is only one reference in the Bible to Coriander (Exodus 16:31), and yet again we must leave scholars discussing the finer points of translation because Coriander certainly doesn't grow in desert conditions. It is interesting to speculate how quail arrived each evening too, although it is said that this phenomenon does occur when large flocks become exhausted in their flight over deserts and have to make unscheduled landings. Coriander has not been an inspiration for poetry, and it isn't mentioned in great literature, but it is a useful addition to our list of herbs, for culinary, medicinal, and even perfumery purposes.

The Romans were responsible for bringing Coriander to Britain, but ancient Egyptians and Greeks are known to have cultivated the herb for medicinal purposes, as did the Chinese.

Uses in modern herbal medicine

Coriander is a carminative. It can be combined with other medicines to disguise an unpleasant taste or to reduce 'griping' side effects. An infusion of Coriander acts as a stimulant and can be helpful in anorexia.

Cystitis and urinary tract infections, allergic skin conditions and hay fever often respond to this herb and, because of its relaxing action on muscles and sphincters of the gut, it is useful as an ingredient of gripe water for babies.

Coriander tea can act as a stimulant in anorexia and fatigue, and chewing the seeds sweetens the breath of sufferers from halitosis.

Coriander has anti-fungal properties and is known to be of use against certain food poisonings by suppressing their absorption in the tissues. There is some (Japanese) research which suggests that this may also apply to lead poisoning.

'WHAT IS IT?'

There were great celebrations after Israel's dramatic deliverance from the Egyptians (see the Song of Moses and Miriam in Exodus 15), but the euphoria was short-lived. First of all, the people complained about the lack of water in the desert – or at least there was water, but it was bitter. The people grumbled to Moses, who cried out to God, who showed him a piece of wood which, when it was thrown into the water, made the water sweet. Then God guided them to Elim, where there were twelve springs and seventy palm trees, and they camped there near the water.

However, when the Israelites left Elim and were crossing the desert to get to Sinai, the whole community grumbled against Moses because of the food. So, again, Moses spoke to God, who promised to rain down bread from heaven for them in the morning and to provide meat for them each evening.

'That evening quail came and covered the camp, and in the morning there was a layer of dew around the camp. When the dew was gone, thin flakes like frost on the ground appeared on the desert floor . . .'

When the Israelites saw it, they said to each other, "What is it?" because they had never seen anything like it. Moses said to them, "It is the bread the Lord has given you to eat."

Each morning everyone gathered as much as he needed, and when the sun grew hot, it melted away. **The people of Israel called the bread manna[1]. It was white like coriander seed and tasted like wafers made with honey . . . The Israelites ate the manna for forty years, until they came to a land that was settled; they ate manna until they reached the border of Canaan.'**

'Then the whole community set out again, and they travelled from place to place as God commanded them. They camped at Rephidim, but there was no water for them to drink, so they quarrelled with Moses:

"Why did you bring us out of Egypt to make us and our children and livestock die of thirst?" they grumbled. It got so bad that Moses went and cried out to God, "What am I to do with these people? They are almost ready to stone me."

'The Lord answered Moses, "Walk on ahead of the people. Take with you some of the elders of Israel, and take in your hand the staff with which you struck the Nile and go. I will stand there before you by the rock at Horeb. Strike the rock, and water will come out of it for the people to drink." So Moses did this in the sight of the elders of Israel. And he called the place Massah[2] and Meribah[3] because the Israelites quarrelled and because they tested the Lord saying, "Is the Lord among us or not.'"

[1] Manna means *What is it?*

[2] Massah means *testing.*

[3] Meribah means *quarrelling.*

Garlic ~ (*Allium sativum*)

Plant description

Garlic, a member of the Onion family, is a particularly pungent herb, its smell being distinctive and unmistakable. The leaves of *Allium sativum* closely resemble grass and the spherical flowerhead, carried on a single stem, has many tiny purple flowers clustered tightly together. It blooms in late summer. The garlic bulb – the edible part of the plant – grows just sub-soil and consists of multiple 'cloves', each one of which is individually wrapped in a fine silvery-purple skin. The bulb itself is enveloped in a courser, papery, whiteish covering. The characteristic smell is only released when the plant is crushed. Garlic is one of the easiest herbs to grow, undemanding as to soil or site, and the flavour of fresh garlic is far superior to any that can be bought.

Plant lore

Garlic probably originated in Asia, but now seems to be cultivated everywhere. It has been used in the kitchen for as long as anyone can remember to flavour dishes of meat, fish and vegetables. It can be added to butter, to salads and to their dressings.

Culinary use for garlic has been known for thousands of years, and so has its medicinal use, and some interesting discoveries have been made more recently: An Egyptian papyrus of 1600BC tells us that workers building the pyramids went on strike because their daily food rations did not include garlic. The garlic was required for their general health, but it is now thought that it would have helped to prevent diseases from water-borne organisms (such as those causing amoebic dysentery). Garlic has been found in the tombs of the pharaohs. The ancient Greeks and Romans are known to have used it as medicine.

In the middle ages, garlic was taken against the plague and against leprosy, although perhaps that was wishful thinking born of desperation. Somewhat later, Culpeper listed a myriad uses for 'the poor man's treacle' – including having drunk Wolf'sbane, Henbane, Hemlock or other poisonous herbs. What a pity poor old Socrates didn't know about that. Garlic was also thought to protect a house from vampires.

Uses in modern herbal medicine

Some 5000 years ago someone recorded a recipe for the use of garlic as a medicine – in cuneiform. Traditional uses of garlic have been confirmed by modern science and there can be no doubt about the efficacy of its use.

Garlic has been widely used in the United Kingdom and Europe for treating many different conditions, including colds, coughs, catarrh, rhinitis and also high cholesterol levels leading to hypertension. Research carried out at the end of the last century confirmed these actions: One group began on a diet high in saturated fats and were then given a clove of garlic each day; the control group were put on the same diet, high in saturated fats, but were not given any garlic. At the end of the six-week trial, the groups were tested. Individuals in the control group were found to have considerably higher blood cholesterol levels than the group who had been taking garlic. Researchers concluded that garlic did in some way protect the heart and circulatory system from increased blood cholesterol levels. Also, compounds in garlic were found to prevent thrombocyte aggregation, a process that decreases the risk of blood clotting and thrombus formation.

Professor Edzard Ernst, a man with the great gift of presenting complex principles in a way that can be easily understood (even by those with no medical training) has put the case for garlic in a book *How Garlic Protects Your Heart* (published by Amberwood in 1996 and still available). It is a perfect mix of scholarship and good sense. As well as dealing, very simply, with the heart and the circulation of the blood, with coronary heart disease and the factors that cause cardiovascular dysfunction and with therapy and prevention of disease, there are short chapters on the efficacy of garlic as a herbal drug, its effects on the cardiovascular system and results from medical research. Professor Ernst deals with the questions of side effects (reassuringly few – odour on the breath being small price to pay for its benefits to health!), indications for taking garlic, dosage, and so on.

Even for those who have no known cardiac disease, garlic has a number of additional beneficial effects that help to prevent disease. 'High blood pressure and diabetes are other risk factors: garlic is known, significantly, to lower mildly elevated blood pressure, and there is some evidence that it normalises blood glucose levels in diabetic patients. It also improves blood flow by making blood more fluid and blood cells less 'sticky'; it has been shown to influence the clotting of blood in such a way that thromboses are less likely to form and more likely to be dissolved if they do form an obstruction . . .'

In conclusion, Professor Ernst writes: 'Garlic has stood the "test of time". It is a very safe and effective means of positively influencing accepted risk factors of coronary heart disease. It can therefore help to protect the heart from arteriosclerosis. Its most notable effects are a normalisation of the lipid profile of the blood. Garlic has been tested extensively in animals, volunteers and patients. It has considerable potential in the prevention of cardiovascular disease and death.'

But there is a caution, even with this wonder herb: Garlic supplements should not be taken with anti-coagulants or with prescription drugs for low blood sugar. This also applies to those being treated for HIV, since it interferes with the action of their prescription drugs.

DISCONTENT IN THE DESERT

The Israelites are not happy, which is not an unusual state of affairs. It is difficult to imagine what would make them even fairly content with their lot. God is going to keep them wandering about in the Sinai peninsula until they obey his laws, until they learn to depend on him totally, and *until they stop complaining!* It is going to take forty years. One man, Moses, seems to have a good relationship with 'Yahweh': Moses has become God's spokesman, his go-between. Moses was the one chosen to lead Israel out of captivity, but the Israelites are people with defective memories. They remember their days in Egypt as idyllic; they consider these days of freedom in the desert making their way to the Promised Land worse than their ill treatment by a tyrannical pharaoh. Just listen to them!

'The rabble with them began to crave other food, and again the Israelites started wailing and said, **"If only we had meat to eat! We remember the fish we ate in Egypt at no cost – also the cucumbers, melons, leeks, onions and garlic.** But now we never see anything but this manna.' (Numbers 11:5-6)

The cucumbers they longed for in the Sinai Desert were *cucumis chate*, and even the Hebrew word describes them well – quishshu – which means 'hard and difficult to digest'. What they had eaten in captivity in Egypt and what they 'remembered' in the desert were very different things.

This is not the first time they have complained about the food provided and Moses is sick of them, so much so that he cries out to God: "Why have you brought this trouble on your servant? What have I done to displease you that you put the burden of all these people on me? Did I conceive all these people? Did I give them birth? . . . Where can I get meat for all these people? . . . I cannot carry all these people by myself; the burden is too heavy for me. If this is how you are going to treat me, put me to death right now . . ." (Numbers 11:11-15)

Poor Moses. God calms him down and says that he will provide meat for everyone and he sends Moses with a message to the people – a message that Moses probably enjoyed giving them: "Now the Lord will give you meat, and you will eat it. You will not eat it for just one day, or two days, or five, ten or twenty days, but for a whole month – until it comes out of your nostrils and you loathe it – because you have rejected the Lord, who is among you, and have wailed before him saying, 'Why did we ever leave Egypt?' " (Numbers 11:18-20)

Moses had seen many miracles: ten plagues in Egypt, the parting of the waters of the Red Sea, water from rock, manna from heaven, God in the pillar of cloud by day and the pillar of fire by night, but he couldn't see how this promise (threat) was to be fulfilled. Incredulous, and still upset by all the discontent, he went back to God. He said, "Here I am among six hundred thousand men on foot, and you say, 'I will give them meat to eat for a whole month.' Would they have enough if flocks and herds were slaughtered for them? Would they have enough if all the fish in the sea were caught for them?"

The Lord answered Moses, "Is the Lord's arm too short? You will now see whether or not what I say will come true for you." (Numbers 11:21-23)

'. . . Now a wind went out from the Lord and drove quail in from the sea. It brought them down all around the camp to about three feet above the ground, as far as a day's walk in any direction. All that day and night and all the next day the people went out and gathered quail . . . but while the meat was still between their teeth and before it could be consumed, the anger of the Lord burned against the people and he struck them with a severe plague. Therefore the place was named Kibroth Hattaavah, because there they buried the people who had craved for other food.' (Numbers 11:31-34)

Kibroth Hattaavah means *graves of craving*. This did nothing to cure the Israelites, of course; they continued to spend their lives complaining to Moses about God. If they had learned to trust much earlier they probably wouldn't have had to spend forty years wandering around the same desert, which could have been crossed in a matter of weeks.

Almond ~ (*Prunus dulcis*)

Plant description

The almond is a small-to-medium sized tree, between 5-10m in height, with dark brown bark and long, finely toothed, lanceolate leaves. It is one of the earliest trees to flower, its mass of fragrant pink blossom appearing as a welcome harbinger of spring about the beginning of March, before the appearance of any leaf. The almond is of the Rose family and is related to the peach and the plum.

Almond flowers each have a bell-shaped calyx, a spreading corolla, some 20 stamens and a pistil, and they are pollinated by honey-bees who appear delighted by this early bounty.

The almond nut itself is contained within a flattened green fruit. On ripening, the fleshy pericarp dries and splits into separate valves, releasing the seed (nut). Within the nutshell, the kernels are covered by a fine brown skin. The nuts can be eaten raw, or crushed to add to food (particularly delicious in marzipan), or they can be roasted.

Plant lore

Cultivation of the almond has its origins back in the mists of time so that we cannot be sure where it originated, but Asia is the most likely place. The almond of Scripture was a rather more scrubby bush, its flowers white, growing in wild and rocky places in Israel and throughout the Middle East. The almond in full flower in those desolate places after a long winter would have stirred the hearts of any traveller.

The candelabrum for the Tabernacle in the Tent of Meeting in the Sinai Desert was decorated with carved almond blossom and its Hebrew name: *shaked* also means new life emerging from death; resurrection; awakening.

Strangely, there is little to be found in poetry about the almond, but the very word brings to mind its distinctive taste and smell and shape. 'Almond-eyed' conjures up a picture of someone exotically oriental and beautiful.

There is a lovely legend about St Francis of Assisi, who was a joyful character in spite of the harsh life of poverty he led with his Brothers. One day, *Il poverello*, the little poor man, was very happy because he saw

God in all creatures. He danced through the streets of the town, singing and inviting everyone to sing and dance with him. He came upon an almond tree and begged it to speak to him of God – and the almond tree blossomed.

Kazantzakis, in his book 'Zorba the Greek', has his narrator walking in bleak winter, a great weight on his shoulders. He sees trees in bud, and in a sheltered hollow an almond tree already in flower. He gives a cry of joy and oppression leaves him. He is in Paradise. He strokes the trunk of the almond tree which contains so many mysteries and has produced this miracle of blossom.

Uses in modern herbal medicine

Almonds are unusually rich in fat – somewhere in the region of 50 % - and they have been widely used in herbal medicine for a very long time.

Almond oil, being light, non-greasy and clear, has many uses: It is an important component of ointments; aromatherapists use it as a vehicle for their essential oils to facilitate application to the skin by massage; babies' bottoms are soothed and kept from soreness by its nice soft, emollient properties; and it is used to soften hardened wax in the ears. Almond oil has so many uses that it would be a good thing to keep in the medicine cabinet or first-aid box at home.

THE BUDDING OF AARON'S STAFF

We are still in the Sinai desert with the Israelites, and they are still grumbling. Moses is still trying to keep all the different tribes in some sort of order, and it is not an easy task. However, this time the trouble is not about food, or lack of variety in their diet. It is much more serious. It is about holiness. It is about who should minister to the people as priests. It is about getting into the inner sanctuary of the Tent of Meeting, into the place where the Tabernacle rests. It is about ruling the Israelites.

Three young men, Korah, Dathan and Abiram spread discontent among the people. They gathered together 250 of the community leaders and as a group they came to challenge Moses and Aaron. The men were insolent, accusing Moses and Aaron of setting themselves higher than the assembly of the people, of thinking that they were holier than anyone else.

Moses had tolerated a great deal from the Israelites and he was so upset that he threw himself down on the ground. Then Moses tried to reason with them, but it turned into a heated argument and he had to give up.

It was a very angry Moses who spoke to God: "Do not accept their offering," he said. "I have not taken so much as a donkey from them, nor have I wronged any of them."

To cut a long and rather messy story short, the rebels and their families were killed when the ground split apart under their feet and the earth swallowed them up. This terrified the rest of the Israelites, but they still grumbled at Moses and Aaron, holding them responsible for the deaths.

Moses was not the only one whose anger burned against the Israelites. God himself had heard enough wrangling and the next day . . . 'When the assembly gathered in opposition to Aaron and Moses and turned towards the Tent of Meeting, suddenly the cloud covered it and the glory of the Lord appeared.' (Numbers 16:42)

God told Moses to stand aside. He was about to kill all the Israelites and be done with them, and in fact a plague had already begun to run through the camp. But Moses was horrified; he told Aaron to take his censer, to fill it with incense and with fire from the altar and to hurry to make atonement for the people. Aaron did as Moses said: he offered incense and made atonement for the people. He stood between the living and the dead, and the plague stopped.

To put an end to any further argument, God told Moses to speak to the Israelites. He was to take twelve staffs from them, one from the leader of each of the twelve ancestral tribes. Moses was to write the name of each man on his staff. On the staff of Levi, Aaron's name was to be written. The staffs were to be placed in the Tent of Meeting, in front of the Ark – the most holy place, where God was. God said that the staff belonging to the man of his choice would sprout, and that was to be the end of all dispute and grumbling.

'So Moses spoke to the Israelites, and their leaders gave him twelve staffs, one for the leader of each of their ancestral tribes, and Aaron's staff was among them. Moses placed the staffs before the Lord in the Tent of Testimony.

'The next day, Moses entered the Tent of Testimony and saw that Aaron's staff, which represented the house of Levi, had not

only sprouted but had budded, blossomed and produced almonds. Then Moses brought out all the staffs from the Lord's Presence to all the Israelites. They looked at them, and each man took his staff.

'The Lord said to Moses, "Put back Aaron's staff in front of the Testimony, to be kept as a sign to the rebellious. This will put an end to their grumbling against me, so that they will not die." Moses did as the Lord commanded him.' (Numbers 17)

The Israelites, by now thoroughly frightened and cowed, were amenable to Moses' order that Aaron's sons and his father's family (the Levites) were to be responsible for looking after the Tent of Testimony, but that Aaron alone should be responsible for the care of the sanctuary and the altar. Only Aaron and his sons were to serve as priests. Moses was giving them the service of the priesthood as a gift from God. Anyone else approaching the sanctuary would die. (Numbers 18)

Cassia ~ (*Cinnamomum cassia*)

Plant description
Ratcliffe gives this tree as being of the Laurel family of evergreens growing to a height of some 15m. Its flowers are non-showy, amply branched panicles of yellow/white scentless flowers in spring from leaf axis. 'The bark is smooth, thick and charged with precious resin. 3-5 year old branches are coppiced, the outer bark is then carefully removed in long strips. The fragrant, volatile oil (cinnamic aldehyde) is mixed with resins distilled from the bark, after the art of the apothecary.'

Zohary says that the Cassia is native to East Asia and is widely cultivated, especially in south-eastern China, for its bark, buds and oil, which are exported to world markets.

The word 'cassia' means shrivelled, contracted, to peel and strip off, to bow the head.

Plant lore
After all Job's vicissitudes, when he was again blessed with family and wealth, Job called one of his daughters, Keziah (Cassia). 'And in all the land were no women found so fair as the daughters of Job.'

In Psalm 45 (a wedding song), verse 8 we read:

**'All your robes are fragrant with
myrrh and aloes and cassia;
from palaces adorned with ivory
the music of the strings makes
you glad.**

And in Exodus 30 we are given God's own recipes for sacred anointing oils and incense which include this most precious commodity.

Uses in modern herbal medicine
Cassia bark is a good anti-spasmodic, carminative and antiseptic. Cassia both tastes and smells pleasantly aromatic, somewhat similar to cinnamon and yet distinct – the perfect herb for a jaded appetite.

Cinnamon ~ (*Cinnamomum zeylanicum*)

Plant description

Like Cassia, *Cinnamomum zeylanicum* also belongs to the Laurel family of evergreens and is a native of south-east Asia. The inconspicuous, pale yellow, flowers of cinnamon trees are borne in panicles and have an unexpectedly unpleasant odour; these are followed by ovate, dark purple berries (nutlets). However, the glory of the cinnamon tree lies in its light brown, furrowed bark which, when removed in strips, dries into familiar aromatic quills. Both bark and leaves are distilled for oil, and cinnamon fruits yield an oil which is particularly fragrant when warmed.

Plant lore

Zohary says that the uses for cinnamon are manifold: 'the bark is used to produce a volatile oil; used to flavour sweets, in curry powder, in incense and perfume. *Cinnamomum zeylanicum* is native to Ceylon and the coast of India – brought to the Holy Land from a great distance. Land and sea trade routes for drugs, incenses, perfume existed not only between Mediterranean and Indian coasts, but farther east, joining the ancient 'silk route' between India and the Far East, reaching south-eastern Arabia, the main emporium of the Sabean kingdom for drugs and incense.'

It sounds as if cinnamon had aphrodisiac properties too for in Proverbs 7:17-18 we read:

> **'I have perfumed my bed with myrrh, aloes and cinnamon.**
> **Come, let's drink deep of love till morning;**
> **let's enjoy ourselves with love!**

John Masefield certainly found this herb evocative of the exotic. In his poem, 'Cargoes', he writes of the stately Spanish galleon coming from the Isthmus, dipping through the Tropics by the palm-green shores,

> **'With a cargo of diamonds,**
> **Emeralds, amethysts,**
> **Topazes, and cinnamon, and gold moidores.'**

In Revelation, in the great 'Woe to Babylon' (Chapter 18) there is a list of the city's most precious cargoes – gold, silver, precious stones and pearls; fine linen, purple silk and scarlet cloth; every sort of citron wood, and articles of every kind made of ivory, costly wood, bronze, iron and marble; **cargoes of cinnamon and spice**, of incense, myrrh and frankincense, of wine and olive oil, of fine flour and wheat; cattle and sheep; horses and carriages; and bodies and souls of men. All these will be taken from her (Babylon) and she will fall.

In Exodus 30:23 Cinnamon is one of the ingredients of the holy oils and incense prescribed by God himself: **'Take the finest spices:** of liquid myrrh 500 shekels, **and of sweet-smelling cinnamon half as much.'**

Uses in modern herbal medicine

Cinnamon bark is aromatic, stimulant, astringent and carminative. Its characteristic odour, like its taste, is sweetly aromatic. This is a herb with antifungal, antibacterial and antiviral properties, one which improves the circulation and makes one feel warm.

Cinnamon is a comforting herb which, when ground and added to a hot drink, makes one feel pampered when poorly with a cold or 'flu or a digestive upset.

However, the essential oil of Cinnamon is irritant when applied directly to the skin, and it should never be taken internally.

Frankincense ~ (*Boswellia sacra*)

Plant description

Ratcliffe says, 'Boswellia is a shrubby, multi-branch evergreen tree, bearing spikes of white, five-petal flowers. The plant naturally exudes the fragrant resin through its leaves, twigs and papery bark. Incising the main branches of the boswellia plant greatly increases the flow of resin. The transparent to yellow-coloured resin quickly turns reddish pink on exposure to air.

The Hebrew name for frankincense derives from the white, milk-like colour of the resin and from the whiteness of the smoke the resin produces when fired. The fragrance of burning frankincense is recognised as the finest in the world.'

Plant lore

Zohary says: 'With other costly commodities, frankincense was imported into the Land of Israel by the Phoenicians via the famous spice route across southern Arabia and some of the littoral stations of East Africa, a caravan highway also used for imports from India and farther east.'

'Frankincense' means, literally, 'pure' or 'true' incense. It was used ceremonially by the Egyptians, the Persians, the Babylonians, Hebrews, Greeks and Romans, and is still used as an ingredient of modern incense in some churches where it is used to precede solemn processions, to cleanse the altar at the beginning of Mass, to cense the celebrant as he takes on the icon of Christ and also the people, who through baptism each have a priestly role to play. At Mass, incense indicates the Presence of God to us and our prayers ascending to Him. And so, incense is still burned to purify, and as a symbol of worship.

The prophet Malachi was told to tell the Israelites that God was far from pleased with them and would not accept their offerings but '. . ."My name will be great among the nations, from the rising to the setting of the sun. In every place incense and pure offerings will be brought to my name, because my name will be great among the nations," says the Lord Almighty.' (Mal 1:10-11)

In the Book of Nehemiah (Chapter 13) there is the story of a priest,

Eliashib, who hadn't proper respect for holy things. Eliashib was put in charge of the storerooms of the house of God and, we are told, he was closely associated with a chap called Tobiah.

While Nehemiah was away, Eliashib provided Tobiah with a large room which was used to store grain offerings and incense and temple articles, and tithes of grain, new wine and oil prescribed for the Levites, singers and gatekeepers, as well as the contributions for the priests.

When Nehemiah returned he was furious at the defilement of the room and threw Tobiah out, and all his goods with him. The rooms had to be purified and God's equipment was restored, with grain offerings and incense.

Frankincense is the gift of one of the Magi at Christ's Nativity (Matthew 2:10-11), and in Exodus 30 it is one of the ingredients of God's holy oils and incenses.

Uses in modern herbal medicine

Frankincense has strong antibacterial properties and has been used for fumigation in the past, before the production of our less pleasant and more savage synthetic substances. God knew a thing or two when he ordered its use as a cleansing agent as well as 'holy smoke'.

The essential Oil of Frankincense not only smells like Heaven, but a few drops in a bath promotes a feeling of well-being and deep thought. Mmm . . .

Myrrh ~ (*Commiphora abyssinica*)

Plant description

Ratcliffe says: 'Myrrh is an aromatic resin obtained from the small Commiphora abyssinica bush. The plant grows in wild desert places and survives harsh environmental conditions. It is a deciduous shrub with thorns, growing to about 2m high, with heavily knotted branches.

'The leaves are units of three ovate leaflets; the flowers are small and white, followed by olive-like fruits.

'The plant has the general appearance of having survived extremely hostile growing conditions, yet, notwithstanding such adverse circumstances, it continues to yield precious aromatic resin. The reddish-brown, translucent, tear-drop size nodules of solidified resin are painstakingly gathered by hand two or three times a week.'

Plant lore

All the biblical references to frankincense apply also to myrrh (the wedding song of Psalm 45; the 'Woe of Babylon' in Revelation 18; the gifts of the Magi in Matt 2, the ingredients of holy oils and incense in Exodus 30), but there are places in Scripture where myrrh appears either alone, or with some other herb:

Myrrh was offered to Jesus on the Cross (Mark 15:22-24) 'They brought Jesus to the place called Golgotha (which means the Place of the Skull). **Then they offered him wine mixed with myrrh, but he did not take it.** And they crucified him.'

Nicodemus brought a mixture of myrrh and aloes, with linen cloths, for wrapping the body of Jesus in the tomb (John 19:39-40): 'He (Joseph of Arimathea) was accompanied by Nicodemus, the man who earlier had visited Jesus at night. **Nicodemus brought a mixture of myrrh and aloes, about seventy-five pounds.** Taking Jesus' body, the two of them wrapped it, with the spices, in strips of linen. This was in accordance with Jewish burial customs.'

Uses in modern herbal medicine

Myrrh is stimulant and tonic and antifungal (and particularly useful where 'thrush' is a nuisance). Myrrh makes an excellent gargle for ulcerated mouths, and it has a place in the treatment of leg ulcers.

GOD'S HOLY RECIPES

The story of the Ten Commandments begins in Chapter 19 of the Book of Exodus. God calls Moses up Mount Sinai while the Israelites assemble in the valley, trembling with fear because there is thunder and lightning and the mountain is covered in smoke 'because the Lord descended on to the mountain in fire.' The earth was quaking beneath their feet and there were trumpet blasts. 'And Moses went up into the thick darkness where God was.'

When Moses came down and told the people about God's commandments they all said, "Everything the Lord has said we will do." Moses wrote down for them all that the Lord had said. He built an altar at the foot of the mountain and set up twelve stone pillars representing the twelve tribes of Israel. Then burnt offerings were made and there was a terrific party; the people were happy because they had been adopted as God's special people. Just to make sure they had got the message, Moses took the Book of the Covenant he had written and read it to the people, slowly, so they could absorb it all. And they said: "We will do everything the Lord has said; we will obey."

God called Moses up the mountain again, to receive the tablets of stone with the law and the commandments engraved on them. So Moses left Aaron in charge and climbed the mountain again. 'When Moses went up on the mountain, the cloud covered it, and the glory of the Lord settled on Mount Sinai. For six days the cloud covered the mountain, and on the seventh day the Lord called to Moses from within the cloud. To the Israelites the glory of the Lord looked like a consuming fire on top of the mountain. Then Moses entered the cloud as he went on up the mountain. And he stayed on the mountain forty days and forty nights.' (Exodus 24:15-18)

This time God went into fine detail. He had chosen the Israelites to be his people and he was going to be their God. They must realise that their God was holy, and that he required his people to be holy, like him. That wasn't unreasonable. He had set out his commandments, and the people had promised to obey – the covenant was to work both ways.

On the mountain, Moses listened while God gave detailed instructions for all sorts of things. There was to be an ark to house the tablet engraved with the ten commandments in God's own handwriting. It was to be made of acacia wood, of exact dimensions. It was to be overlaid in gold. Poles of acacia wood, also overlaid with gold, for carrying the ark were to be fitted to four gold rings, two on each side. An atonement cover of pure gold was to be made, with two cherubim of hammered gold at each end of the cover. The cherubim were to have their wings spread upwards to overshadow the atonement cover. The cherubim were to face each other, looking towards the cover. God said, "Place the cover on top of the ark and put in the ark the Testimony (the stone tablets), which I will give you. There, above the cover, between the two cherubim that are over the ark of the Testimony, I will meet with you and give you all my commands for the Israelites."

God told Moses to make a table (again with carrying poles; again with precise measurements), with plates and dishes of gold, as well as pitchers and bowls for the pouring out of offerings. The Bread of the Presence was to be on this table at all times.

There was to be a tabernacle, with curtains of finely twisted linen and blue and purple and scarlet yarn, with cherubim worked into them by skilled craftsmen. Curtains of goat hair were to be made for the tent over the tabernacle – eleven altogether. Five of the curtains were to be joined together in one set, five in another set, and the sixth curtain was to be folded double at the front of the tent. The number of curtain rings and loops were specified; every minute detail was there – frames of the tabernacle, crossbars, fittings, everything. The Ark of the Testimony was to be behind the curtain. The curtain was to separate the Holy Place from the Most Holy Place. The Ark of the Covenant (containing the Ten Commandments) was to be placed in the Most Holy Place. Everything else was to be outside the curtain.

There is the blueprint for the Altar of Burnt Offering, for the courtyard, for the tabernacle. Oil for the lampstand was to be from pressed olives so that the light was always be kept burning as an everlasting ordinance among the Israelites for future generations.

Priestly garments were to be made by skilled craftsmen to whom God had given wisdom in such matters. 'God said, "These are the garments they are to make; a breastpiece, and ephod (Make the robe of the ephod entirely of blue cloth, with an opening for the head in its centre. There shall be a woven edge like a collar around this opening, so that it will not tear. Make pomegranates of blue, purple and scarlet yarn around the hem of the robe, with gold bells between them. The gold bells and the pomegranates are to alternate around the hem of the robe. Aaron must wear it when he ministers. The sound of the bells will be heard when he enters the Holy Place before the Lord and when he comes out, so that he will not die.), a robe, a woven tunic, a turban and a sash. They are to make these **sacred** garments for your brother Aaron and his sons, so that they may serve me as priests. Make them use gold, and blue, purple and scarlet yarn, and fine linen." '

There are details about the consecration of priests before they can serve before the Lord, and details of the building of an altar for burning incense, and much more. Even the anointing oils and the incense have precise recipes:

ANOINTING OIL: **'Then the Lord said to Moses, "Take the following fine spices: 500 shekels of liquid myrrh, half as much (that is 250 shekels) of fragrant cinnamon, 250 shekels of fragrant cane, 500 shekels of cassia – all according to the sanctuary shekel – and a hin of olive oil. Make these into a sacred anointing oil, a fragrant blend, the work of a perfumer. It will be the sacred anointing oil. Then use it to anoint the Tent of Meeting, the Ark of the Testimony, the table and all its articles, the lampstand and its accessories, the altar of incense, the altar of burnt offering and all its utensils, and the basin with its stand. You shall consecrate them so they will be most holy, and whatever touches them will be holy.**

"Anoint Aaron and his sons and consecrate them so they may serve me as priests. Say to the Israelites, 'This is to be my sacred anointing oil for the generations to come. Do not pour it on men's bodies and do not make any oil with the same formula. It is sacred, and you are to consider it sacred. Whoever makes perfume like it and whoever puts it on anyone other than a priest must be cut off from his people.' " (Exodus 30:22-33)

INCENSE: **'Then the Lord said to Moses, "Take fragrant spices – gum, resin, onycha and galbanus – and pure frankincense, all in**

equal amounts, and make a fragrant blend of incense, the work of a perfumer. It is to be salted and pure and sacred. Grind some of it to powder and place it in front of the Testimony in the Tent of Meeting, where I will meet with you. It shall be most holy to you. Do not make any incense with this formula for yourselves; consider it holy to the Lord. Whoever makes any like it to enjoy its fragrance must be cut off from the people." ' (Exodus 30:34-38)

A shekel = about 12 pounds (about 6 kilograms).
A hin = about 4 litres (approx 6½ pints)

Moses had been gone for forty days and forty nights – which is the biblical way of saying, a very long time. God knew that some very unholy things were happening down in the valley and he warned Moses to expect trouble: 'Then the Lord said to Moses, "Go down, because your people, whom you brought up out of Egypt, have become corrupt. They have been quick to turn away from what I commanded them and have made them- selves an idol cast in the shape of a calf. They have bowed down to it and sacrificed to it"

God said he felt so angry that he had half a mind to destroy the Israelites and be done with it, but Moses pleaded for them, reminding God of his promises. Then God, who was really rather fond of Moses, relented. So, 'Moses turned and went down the mountain with the two tablets of the Testimony in his hands. They were inscribed on both sides, front and back. The tablets were the work of God; the writing was the writing of God, engraved on the tablets.'

Moses could hear singing and shouting before he could even see the camp, but as he got nearer he saw the golden calf and people dancing around it, and he was as angry as God had been. He threw the tablets down so that they broke into pieces at the foot of the mountain. He took the calf they had made and burned it in the fire; then he ground it to powder, scattered it on the water and made the Israelites drink it. He was even angry with his brother Aaron for not stopping the people from worshipping a false god. Poor Aaron.

' "Do not be angry with me, my lord," Aaron answered. "You know how prone these people are to evil. They said to me, 'Make us gods who will go before us. As for this fellow, Moses who brought us up out of Egypt, we don't know what has happened to him.' So I told them, "Whoever has any gold jewellery, take it off." Then they gave me the gold, and I threw it into the fire, and out came this calf!" '

Moses trudged back up Mount Sinai to beg forgiveness for the sins of his people, and again God relented and forgave them. Then something wonderful happened for Moses – he became God's friend. God said to him, "I know you by name and you have found favour with me." And later we read (in Exodus 33:11) that 'The Lord would speak to Moses, face to face, as a man speaks with a friend.'

God asked Moses to chisel out two new stone tablets, like the ones broken on the mountain, and God wrote on them the same words, and: 'When Moses came down from Mount Sinai with the two tablets in his hands, he was not aware that his face was radiant because he had spoken with the Lord. When Aaron and all the Israelites saw Moses, his face was radiant, and they were afraid to come near him . . . When Moses finished speaking to them he put a veil over his face. But whenever he entered the Lord's presence to speak with him, he removed the veil until he came out.'

And so, the Israelites made the ark to house the two tablets of stone, and the table, the lampstand, the altar of incense and the altar of burnt offering, and the basin for washing, and the courtyard, and the priestly garments, and they set up the tabernacle, the Tent of Meeting. 'Then Moses set up the courtyard around the tabernacle and altar and put up the curtain at the entrance to the courtyard. And so Moses finished the work.

'Then the cloud covered the Tent of Meeting, and the glory of the Lord filled the tabernacle . . . In all the travels of the Israelites, whenever the cloud lifted from above the tabernacle, they would set out; but if the cloud did not lift, they did not set out – until the day it lifted. So the cloud of the Lord was over the tabernacle by day, and fire was in the cloud by night, in the sight of all the house of Israel during all their travels.' (Exodus 40)

Willow ~ (*Salix alba. Salix acmophylla*)

Plant description

Ratcliffe says: 'The willow belongs to the family Salicaceae, comprised of two genera – salix and populus. Around 400 species make up the salix genus, but only a few are native to Palestine . . . Most botanists have concluded that the biblical willow is either salix acmophylla or salix alba, or that even both species may have been referred to at different times. Willows are deciduous trees, also diecious, that is, the male and female flowers are borne on separate trees; the flowers are very simple, having neither sepals nor petals. Unlike the catkins on the poplar that hang down against the growth of the branch, the catkins on a willow are erect – a useful identity tip. The habitat of willows is the moist plains of the Jordan Valley and by the banks of rivers. The fast-growing, flexible growths of the willows (called withies) are ideal for making baskets and mats; but the children of Israel were required to use them for something far more important . . .'

And Zohary says: 'The two native species of willow are rather common along the banks of permanent streams and near fresh-water springs, in the Coastal Plain, on the mountains and in the upper Jordan Valley. The differences between them are often blurred by hybridization, but *S. alba* is in general a northern species demanding a cooler climate than *S. acmophylla*, which is more heat-tolerant. In the forest along the Jordan River, willows dominate in the north where the water is fresh, and towards the south give way to the Euphrates poplar, which is tolerant of salt water.

'The willow is a deciduous tree with oblong acute leaves shed at the end of summer . . .'

Plant lore

The willow tree is the main feature of Thomas Turner's blue and white porcelain (which imitated the Chinese style of decoration) and gives it the familiar name: Willow Pattern.

Cricket bats are made of willow and cricket balls of stitched leather (hence the nostalgic 'sound of leather on willow' redolent of English summer afternoons on the village green). The 'Cricket Bat Willow', *S. coerulea*, (so called because of its bluish leaves) is grown specially for the purpose.

Traditionally, the weeping willow (*S. chrysocoma*) has been associated with sorrow and with mourning and it is probably the most easily identifiable tree in gardens and the countryside. It is stunning when its fronds trail in a lake or stream, or when sun strikes it against a backdrop of grey sky.

In the Bible, the willow is often associated with water and desirable streams, e.g: 'For I will pour my spirit upon your descendants, and my blessings on your offspring. They shall spring up like a green tamarisk, **like willows by flowing streams.**' (Isaiah 44:3-4 NRSV)

Uses in modern herbal medicine
This most valuable herb is anti-inflammatory, analgesic, antipyretic, antirheumatic and astringent.

White Willow extract has been used from time immemorial for medicinal purposes.

Hippocrates (Greek physician and 'Father of medicine' c 460-357BC) prescribed it in obstetrics, and Dioscorides recorded its uses in the lst century AD, but it was not until the early 1800s that clinical research was undertaken seriously.

Chevallier says that salicin was first isolated from White Willow in 1838, becoming the forerunner of aspirin (acetylsalicylic acid), and first produced as a chemical in 1899. Salicin, (and the phenolic glycosides in general) have similar analgesic and anti-inflammatory properties to aspirin – relieving pain and reducing fevers. However, since salicin is absorbed in the duodenum rather than in the stomach, no irritation of the gastric mucosa occurs, but salicin does not have the blood-thinning properties of aspirin.

Those allergic to aspirin should avoid Willow Bark, and Willow in any form should be avoided by those taking anticoagulant drugs.

The bark from young branches is used for decoctions, capsules and tinctures, but our friend, Dioscorides, suggested taking 'Willow leaves, mashed with a little pepper and drunk with wine to relieve lower back pain.' Sounds good.

Chevallier says that Willow Bark is specific for rheumatic and arthritic inflammation and for pain brought on by such inflammation (or degeneration) . . . It may also be used for gout, ankylosing spondylitis and psoriatic arthropathy.

Willow Bark is often combined with other herbs – with Celery seed for osteo-arthritis; with Devil's Claw and/or Black Cohosh for rheumatoid and other forms of inflammatory arthritis; with Feverfew for headache and migraine, and with Peppermint as an antipyretic.

Both salicin and its synthetic counterpart, aspirin, have found a valuable place in the prevention of deep vein thrombosis and in reducing the risk of heart attack and 'stroke'.

FEASTING AND FASTING

At first sight, Leviticus, the third book of the Pentateuch, is daunting; full of taboos and precise instructions about burnt offerings and grain offerings, fellowship offerings, sin offerings and guilt offerings. Strict dietary restrictions are set, priests are ordained, and purification ceremonies are described in minute detail. There are regulations about infectious diseases, mildew, unlawful sex, and so on, and so on.

Leviticus is, above all, about purity and impurity. It is about holiness, the holiness of God who desires that his people should be holy as he is holy. Here we meet the Almighty God, the One who cannot be imagined. Here Israel is made aware that their God Is totally 'other' than anything in the ordinary world of their human experience.

But, if God lays down rules, he is also lavish with great gifts to his people. He orders seven great feasts (seven being the number of completion in the Jewish tradition), which are still observed today, albeit in modified form. They all commemorate some great deed of God, for example, Creation, Deliverance from Egypt, Harvest, and all are to be found in the 23rd chapter of the book of Leviticus:

THE SABBATH: 'There are six days when you may work, but the seventh day is a Sabbath of rest, a day of sacred assembly. You are not to do any work; wherever you live, it is a Sabbath to the Lord.'

THE PASSOVER AND UNLEAVENED BREAD: 'The Lord's Passover begins at twilight on the fourteenth day of the first month[(1)]. On the fifteenth day of that month the Lord's Feast of Unleavened Bread begins; for seven days you must eat bread made without yeast. On the first day hold a sacred assembly and do no regular work. For seven days present an offering made to the Lord by fire. And on the seventh day hold a sacred assembly and do no regular work.'

FIRST FRUITS: 'The Lord said to Moses, "Speak to the Israelites and say to them: 'When you enter the land I am going to give you and you reap its harvest, bring to the priest a sheaf of the first grain you harvest. He is to wave the sheaf before the Lord so it will be accepted on your behalf; the priest is to wave it on the day after the Sabbath. On the day you wave the sheaf, you must sacrifice as a burnt offering to the Lord a lamb a year old without defect, together with its grain offering of two-tenths of an ephah[(2)] of fine flour mixed with oil – an offering made to the Lord by fire, a pleasing aroma – and its drink offering of a quarter of a hin[(3)] of wine. You must not eat any bread, or roasted or new grain, until the very day you bring this offering to your God. This is to be a lasting ordinance for the generations to come, wherever you live." '

FEAST OF WEEKS: 'From the day after the Sabbath, the day you brought the sheaf of the wave offering, count off seven full weeks. Count off fifty days up to the day after the seventh Sabbath, and then present an offering of new grain to the Lord. From wherever you live, bring two loaves made of two-tenths of an ephah of fine flour, baked with yeast, as a wave offering of firstfruits to the Lord . . .

When you reap the harvest of your land, do not reap to the very edges of your field or gather the gleanings of your harvest. Leave them for the poor and the alien. I am the Lord your God.'

THE FEAST OF TRUMPETS: 'The Lord said to Moses, "Say to the Israelites: On the first day of the seventh month you are to have a day of rest, a sacred assembly commemorated with trumpet blasts. Do no regular work, but present an offering made to the Lord by fire." '

THE DAY OF ATONEMENT *(Yom Kippur: the only day in the year when the priest could go beyond the Temple veil, to obtain remission of sins for the people):* 'The Lord said to Moses, "The tenth day of this seventh month is the Day of Atonement. Hold a sacred assembly and deny yourselves, and present an offering made to the Lord by fire. Do not work on that day, because it is the Day of Atonement, when atonement is made for you before the Lord your God. Anyone who does not deny himself on that day must be cut off from his people. I will destroy from among his people anyone who does any work on that day. You shall do no work at all. This is to be a lasting ordinance for the generations to come, wherever you live. It is a sabbath of rest for you, and you must deny yourselves. From the evening of the ninth day of the month until the following evening you are to observe your sabbath." '

THE FEAST OF TABERNACLES: 'The Lord said to Moses, "Say to the Israelites: 'On the fifteenth day of the seventh month the Lord's Feast of Tabernacles begins, and it is to last for seven days. The first day is a sacred assembly; do no regular work. For seven days present offerings made to the Lord by fire, and on the eighth day hold a sacred assembly and present an offering made to the Lord by fire. It is the closing assembly; do no regular work . . .

"So, beginning with the fifteenth day of the seventh month, after you have gathered the crops of the land, celebrate the festival to the Lord for seven days; the first day is a day of rest, and the eighth day also is a day of rest. On the first day you are to take choice fruit from the trees, and palm fronds, leafy branches and poplars (willows), and rejoice before the Lord your God for seven days. Celebrate this as a festival to the Lord for seven days each year. This is to be a lasting ordinance for the generations to come; celebrate it in the seventh month. Live in booths for seven days: All native-born Israelites are to live in booths so your descendants will know that I made the Israelites live in booths when I brought them out of Egypt. I am the Lord your God."

'So Moses announced to the Israelites the appointed feasts of the Lord.'

[1] September in our present Gregorian calendar.
[2] Probably about 4.5 litres.
[3] Probably about one litre.

3 | The Deuteronomic History

What a dreary title! And it gives no indication of what we are to expect in the great 600-year epic of the books of **Joshua**, **Judges**, **Samuel** and **Kings**.

At the end of Deuteronomy we left the Israelites massed on the Plain of Moab, in sight of the Promised Land. Moses is dead. It is the end of an era. God is about to do a new thing. But the Israelites have not changed; they repeatedly turn from God and have to be dragged back to fidelity to Yahweh. This history begins on the banks of the Jordan on the day the Israelites are to enter Canaan, and it ends with the terrible destruction of the Temple at Jerusalem and exile in Babylon.

Joshua: First of all, God tells Joshua that he is now leader (not a great surprise since he has been Moses' deputy for some time and knows all the foibles of his charges). Joshua is to lead the Israelites into a new life across the Jordan River. He has the same promises of God's care and protection (and the same stipulations of faithfulness). "Be strong and courageous, because you will lead these people to inherit the land I swore to their forefathers to give them . . . Be careful to obey all the law my servant Moses gave you; do not turn from it to the right or to the left, that you may be successful wherever you go. Do not let this Book of the Law depart from your mouth; meditate on it day and night, so that you may be careful to do everything written in it. Then you will be prosperous and successful . . . Do not be terrified; do not be discouraged, for the Lord your God will be with you wherever you go." (Joshua 1:6-9).

All of which sounds wonderful. The Israelites cross the Jordan, with the priests carrying the Ark of the Covenant before them (not easy since at that time of year the river was in full flood, but as soon as the Ark reached the river-bank the waters receded and they all went across, dry-shod). But one small problem presents itself immediately: Canaan, the land flowing with milk and honey is already occupied and the Israelites are soon engaged in combat without the help of much weaponry. In Joshua, chapter six, we have the wonderful story of 'Joshua at the Battle of Jericho' when the walls came tumbling down at the blast of trumpets. 'So the Lord was with Joshua, and his fame spread throughout the land.'

Judges begins with the death of Joshua before covering a 200-year period between the settlement in Canaan and the beginning of monarchy. After Joshua's death we read that a generation grew up who didn't know the Lord, or what he had done for Israel, so the Israelites fell by the wayside and worshipped Baal. So 'God raised up judges in the land.' These judges were charismatic figures who rose from the ranks of the people in time of need to lead in war or to guide in time of peace. The appearances of some are fleeting; others are famous and rule for many years. In these 21 chapters we meet the prophetess Deborah, who saved Israel from its enemies; Gideon (of whom more later), Tola, son of Puah, 'who rose to save Israel'; Jephthah the Gileadite, who was also a mighty warrior (in spite of his mother being a prostitute); Samson (who had trouble with a girl called Delilah and a haircut), who defeated the Philistines even when they had gouged out his eyes and he couldn't see.

The book of Judges ends with the words: 'In those days Israel had no king; everyone did as he saw fit.'

Ruth: There are just four chapters in the Book of Ruth and, strictly speaking, they are not part of the deuteronomic history. But somehow it seems entirely right that Ruth should have her place in the midst of all the turmoil of the emergence of a nation, and for another most important reason. 'Ruth' is a love story; a story of loyalty, of courage born of great necessity. It is an oasis in all the hurly-burly of wars, famines, pestilences, intrigues and great deeds of cunning and strength. Ruth, a gentile and a woman, and therefore of little account in Jewish history on two counts is, nevertheless, mentioned *by name* in St Matthew's great genealogy of Jesus right there in the first chapter of his gospel. (**'. . . Boaz, the father of Obed, whose mother was Ruth, Obed the father of Jesse, and Jesse the father of King David . . . and Jacob the father of Joseph, the husband of Mary, of whom was born Jesus, who is called**

Christ.') And Matthew is an archetypal Jew! 'Ruth' is a gentle story with a happy ending which we shall read more fully a little later . . .

The Two Books of Samuel were originally just one book. Samuel is the last judge in Israel (and he doesn't look forward to relinquishing the role with any great joy). However, there is increasing pressure and threat from the Philistines and the Israelites want a king to rule over them 'like all the other nations'. God tells Samuel to anoint a king for the people, but he is to point out all the disadvantages of monarchy too (I Samuel 8:10-18). 'But the people refused to listen to Samuel. "No!" they said. "We want a king over us. Then we shall be like all the other nations, with a king to lead us and to go out before us and fight our battles." When Samuel heard all that the people said, he repeated it before the Lord. The Lord answered, "Listen to them and give them a king."

First of all Israel gets Saul as king. Saul starts off well enough but he becomes capricious and unpredictable in temper, a paranoid depressive who has fits of acute melancholy and harbours a murderous hatred of David. When Saul comes to an inglorious end on the battlefield, he is succeeded by David (also anointed king by Samuel). David's reign is Israel's most memorable and celebrated ever. For a short time Israel is a power to be reckoned with. It is a golden age. David does everything with great passion (from his mockery of the giant Goliath before killing him with a single stone from his sling; to his dancing before the Ark; to his affair with Bathsheba and the murder of her husband Uriah; to his very public and very full acknowledgement of his sins before God). This is a wonderful, unabridged version of a great king, but a very human man (unlike the 'edited' accounts of the same events in Chronicles). David and his line hold God's promise of hope for a Messiah.

The Books of the Kings were also originally just one book, covering about four centuries of Israel's history. At the beginning we find the splendour and wisdom of Solomon, then, through a series of bad kings and a falling away from God, we trace the decline of the monarchy, ending with the final destruction of Jerusalem and exile in Babylon. There is the familiar and recurrent pattern (well established back with Moses and the Israelites in the desert), of infidelity on the part of Israel, followed by punishment by God, followed by repentance of the people, followed by deliverance from whatever trouble their sin has landed them in. From wealth, culture, prosperous trade and the building of a wonderful temple fit for Yahweh to live in, the Israelites come to an ignominious end. The moral is clear: When God's laws are obeyed, there is peace and prosperity; when they are not, there is division and collapse. In these pages we meet some of the early prophets, like Elijah and Elisha, those thorns in the flesh of bad kings.

Towards the end of the Second Book of Kings (chapters 22 and 23) there is a moment of calm before the coming storm. Josiah, aged 26, becomes king. 'And he did what was right in the eyes of the Lord and walked in all the ways of his father David, not turning aside to the right or to the left.' – which was a novel idea in those days. Josiah decided to refurbish and reconsecrate the Temple, during which work the Book of the Law was found. Josiah looked at it, realized how far the nation had come from God's commands, and he tore his robes and ordered Israel to do penance. Josiah renewed the Covenant (the recently discovered Book of the Law) and all the people turned to the Lord. 'Neither before nor after Josiah was there a king like him who turned to the Lord as he did – with all his heart and with all his soul and with all his strength, in accordance with the Law of Moses.'

However, when Josiah died, subsequent kings turned from God and in 587BC, Nebuchadnezzar, King of Babylon, marched on Judah and began mass deportations to Babylon. In 586, with only the poorest people who were of little use to the king left, Jerusalem was finally sacked and the Temple was destroyed.

Milk Thistle ~ (*Silybum marianum*)
Holy Thistle ~ (*Cnicus benedictus*)

Plant description

There seems to be a good deal of confusion surrounding these two members of the Compositae family. Many people seem to think that Milk Thistle ('Our Lady's Thistle' or 'Mary's Thistle') and Holy Thistle (or 'Blessed Thistle') are one and the same plant: Most assuredly, they are not. Apart from sharing the prickly characteristics of thistles generally, they are not even similar to look at. Moreover, they behave quite differently, botanically speaking, and they have entirely different properties in the world of herbal medicine. So let us take them as they are – separately.

The Milk Thistle (*Silybum marianum*), is a tall hardy biennial. In its first year it simply forms a rosette of spine-edged, variegated leaves which hug the ground. But in the following year a long, finely-haired stem develops to carry a single bright purple thistle some 5cm (2 inches) across, surrounded by impressive – and wickedly sharp – spiny bracts. In autumn, large dark-brown seeds (more properly nutlets) are borne away on fine silk hair parachutes. These are lovely dramatic plants for a sunny place at the back of the mixed border. As a bonus, goldfinches will come to feast on the ripe seeds.

The Holy Thistle (*Cnicus benedictus*) is an annual with very hairy but much narrower leaves than the Milk Thistle, and by comparison it is short – only attaining a height of some 60cm (2ft). The stems, covered in cobweb-like hairs, are sticky to the touch. Holy Thistle flowers are yellow, only 3–3.5cms across, solitary and surrounded by spiny bracts.

Zohary gives two other kinds of thistle indigenous to the Holy Land: Syrian Thistle (*Notobasis syriaca*) and Globe Thistle (*Echinops viscosus*), which may well have played a part in our story.

Plant lore

The thistle has long been used as the heraldic emblem of Scotland and is often found on insignia there, together with St Andrew and his cross.

Thistles are said to cure a 'stitch' in the side – although it is difficult to see quite how this works. Perhaps the sting of the thistle's spines takes the mind off the original pain!

There is a legend that the Milk Thistle (*S. marianum*) owes the beautiful white markings on its foliage to milk which fell from the Blessed Virgin's breast when she was feeding Jesus.

In the Bible, in the Book of the Judges, Gideon uses thistles to teach the men of Succoth a lesson, punishing them with 'desert thorns and briers'.

Uses in modern herbal medicine

HOLY THISTLE is tonic, carminative, diaphoretic and emmenagogue. The aerial parts are collected when the plant is in flower, then dried and presented as a liquid extract. A warm infusion will 'break a cold' and reduce fever; it will also help menstrual dysfunction.

There is no odour, but the bitter taste of the extract will stimulate taste buds to increase salivation, thereby refreshing a jaded appetite.

Holy Thistle is contra-indicated in pregnancy.

MILK THISTLE: In these days of pollutants, junk food, drug and alcohol abuse and severe infections, our livers take an awful beating and need all the detoxifying we can give them. Even necessary conventional medicine (e.g. chemotherapy) can put this most precious organ under severe stress.

Milk Thistle really is a wonder herb. It protects the liver, helping it to excrete toxins by stimulating bile flow and even contributing to liver cell regeneration. It will also stimulate lactation.

Chevallier says that from 1968 to the present day, research has focused on one constituent (silymarin), which exerts a highly protective effect on the sinusoidal cells of the liver, supporting normal liver function and protecting against substances which would otherwise poison the liver.

Hepatic breakdown and death resulting from ingestion of certain solvents, or of toxins within the Death Cap mushroom, is prevented if silymarin is taken within 20 minutes of the poison being swallowed.

The seeds of the Milk Thistle are used in capsules or in a liquid extract.

Milk Thistle is no newcomer: Dioscorides knew it as *silybon* – 'thistle-like', thus giving the plant its generic name. And Pliny 'the Elder' (23-79AD) recommended it in his massive, 37 volume '*Historia Naturalis*'. A much later user, Gerard, in his '*Herbal*' of 1597, said, 'My opinion is that this is the best remedy that grows against all melancholy diseases.' And, of course, traditionally melancholia has been associated with liver 'disease'.

GIDEON, GOD'S MIGHTY WARRIOR

God has a lovely quirky mind, of that there can be no doubt. Not only does he choose the most unlikely people to do his work, but he seems to enjoy their initial reaction – which is usually a plea of mistaken identity: "You've got the wrong man!" And mostly, on the face of it, they are right; they haven't the required qualifications or abilities, and they are right to be panic-stricken or plain disbelieving. However, when God says, "I will be with you", and he always does, there is no excuse to be found. People end up doing the most amazing things – as much to their own astonishment as anyone else's.

It was like that for Gideon. He was the youngest son of an insignificant family of the half tribe of Manasseh (the other half were lost in the desert and never found). Times were particularly bad just then. After forty years of peace and prosperity, the Israelites had become bored and self-centred and they had worshipped false gods. There was nothing new in that, of course, they seemed programmed for boom and bust. For years they would obey God and prosper, then they would turn from him and he would have to send them a reminder in the form of a plague or a war, or something equally traumatic, so that they cried out to him again and he would rescue them, again. In chapter 6 of the Book of Judges we read:

'Again the Israelites did evil in the eyes of the Lord, and for seven years he gave them into the hands of the Midianites. Because the power of Midian was so oppressive, the Israelites prepared shelters for themselves in mountain clefts, caves and strongholds. Whenever the Israelites planted their crops, the Midianites, Amalekites and other eastern peoples invaded the country. They camped on the land and ruined the crops all the way to Gaza and did not spare a living thing for Israel, neither sheep nor cattle nor donkeys. They came up with their livestock and their tents like swarms of locusts. It was impossible to count the men and their camels; they invaded the land to ravage it. Midian so impoverished the Israelites that they cried out to the Lord for help.'

And so, God sent his angel to the man he had chosen as his new leader to the wilful, wayward Israelites.

Gideon had hidden some wheat in a disused winepress to keep it from the sharp eyes of the invading Midianites, and he was busy threshing it when the angel of the Lord – disguised as a young man – came and sat down by an oak tree beside him. The man had appeared out of nowhere, and Gideon, even with his eyes peeled and ears tuned to the arrival of strangers, had not heard him approach. The young man's greeting probably sounded cynical too: "The Lord is with you, might warrior."

Mighty warrior? Gideon was not slow to point out his irritation with God: "If the Lord is with us, why are we in such a mess? Where are all the wonderful things that our ancestors said we would have, all those promises of a land flowing with milk and honey? No, we have been abandoned to the Midianites; *they* are the mighty warriors. We are nothing."

Then it is no longer the angel, but God speaking to Gideon. The Bible says, 'The Lord turned to him and said, "Go in the strength you have and save Israel out of Midian's hand. Am I not sending you?" Gideon immediately recognized God in the angel: "But Lord," Gideon asked, "How can I save Israel? My clan is the weakest in Manasseh, and I am the least in my family."

Gideon is following the "Who, *me!*" tradition to the letter. But nobody ever gets away with that. The Lord delivers his usual clincher: "I will be with you, and you will strike down all the Midianites together."

It's not that Gideon doesn't believe that God can't do anything he wants, exactly, it's just that he is not the most confident of young men, and the whole thing sounds so far- fetched. So, he plays for time and for confirmation that this is *kosher*, he asks for a sign, just to be sure, you understand. Gideon says, "If now I have found favour in your eyes, give me a sign that it is really you talking to me. Please do not go away until I come back and bring my offering and set it before you." And the Lord, courteous as ever, says, "I will wait until you return."

The Lord must have waited a long time, because 'Gideon went in, prepared a young goat, and from an ephah of flour he made bread without yeast. Putting the meat in a basket and its broth in a pot, he brought them out and offered them to him under the oak.'

No doubt Gideon thought he had prepared a fine meal, but it was never eaten: 'The angel of God said to him, "Take the meat and the unleavened bread, place them on this rock, and pour out the broth." And Gideon did so. With the tip of the staff that was in his hand, the angel of the Lord touched the meat and the unleavened bread. Fire flared from the rock, consuming the meat and the bread. And the angel of the Lord disappeared.'

Well, Gideon had been given his sign, but afterwards, when the angel disappeared in a puff of smoke, he was terrified, because he had seen the angel of the Lord face to face, and he had been taught that no-one does that and lives to tell the tale. However, the angel appears again and tells him not to be afraid, Gideon is not going to die because there is work to be done. Gideon is to take his father's second-best bull and tear down the altar to Baal and cut down the pole dedicated to Baal's wife, Asherah. He is to build a proper altar to the Lord God and, using the wood from the Asherah pole, he is to offer his father's second-best bull as a burnt offering.

Gideon is not yet very brave. He does as he is told by the angel, but at night, hoping no-one will know about his involvement. Investigations are carried out. Gideon is exposed and is condemned to death.

Fortunately for Gideon, his father, Joash, was a God-fearing man who was prepared to speak up for his son. Joash faced the hostile crowd baying for Gideon's blood and he challenged them: "Are you going to plead Baal's cause? If Baal really is a god, he can defend himself when someone breaks down his altar." And so, instead of being lynched, Gideon was applauded by the people.

Gideon has taken his first faltering steps to becoming a mighty warrior, and not a moment too soon. All the Midianites, the Amalekites and other eastern peoples have joined forces; they have crossed the Jordan River and are camped in the Valley of Jezreel. Thousands of them. The besieged Israelites are terrified. But: 'The Spirit of the Lord came upon Gideon, and he blew a trumpet, summoning his allies to follow him. Messengers sent through the whole tribe (half tribe) of Manasseh called them to arms; and men from Asher, Zebulun and Naphtali who had been similarly oppressed (and who had little to lose), came to join them.'

Gideon couldn't believe what was happening, much less what was promised, so he asked God for another sign. Gideon said to God, "If you will save Israel by my hand as you have promised – look, I will place a wool fleece on the threshing floor. If there is a dew only on the fleece and all the ground is dry, then I will know that you will save Israel by my hand, as you said." And that is what happened. Gideon got up early next morning; he squeezed the fleece and wrung out the dew – a bowlful of water.'

Gideon still wasn't sure. It might have been a fluke. He said to God,

"Please don't be angry with me. Let me make just one request. Allow me one more test with the fleece. This time make the fleece dry and the ground covered with dew." God wanted Gideon to be sure, to be confident, and so he did what Gideon asked. The next morning only the fleece was dry; all the ground was covered with dew.

Now Gideon was ready to prepare for battle. Early the next morning, Gideon and all his men went out and camped at the spring of Harod, to the South of the Midian camp in the valley near the hill of Moreh. God was concerned that with the enormous number of Israelites that Gideon had mustered Israel might in future boast that she had won by her own strength. So he said to Gideon, "Announce now to the people, 'Anyone who trembles with fear may turn back and leave.' So twenty-two thousand men left, leaving ten thousand to fight.

'But the Lord said to Gideon, "There are still too many men. Take them down to the water, and I will sift them out for you there. If I say, 'this one shall go with you,' he shall go; but if I say, 'This one shall not go with you,' he shall not go."

Gideon – getting used to doing what he was told – took the men down to the water. God told him to separate those who lapped the water with their tongues like dogs from those who knelt down to drink. Three hundred men lapped with their hands to their mouths. The rest drank on their knees. The ones who drank on their knees were discarded, leaving only three hundred out of the original thirty-two thousand to fight the great battle against the Midianites. Not very good odds.

'Now the camp of Midian lay below him in the valley. During that night the Lord said to Gideon, "Get up, go down against the camp, because I am going to give it into your hands. If you are afraid to attack, go down to the camp with your servant, Purah, and listen to what they are saying. Afterwards, you will be encouraged to attack the camp."

Gideon was afraid, so he took the second option. He and Purah went down to the outposts of the enemy camp. 'The Midianites, the Amalekites and all the other eastern peoples had settled in the valley, thick as locusts. Their camels could no more be counted than the sand on the sea-shore.' It was a terrifying sight and poor Gideon wanted to turn and run, but God said he would be with them, and he had done some marvellous things so far, so . . .

Gideon and Purah went out under cover of darkness to spy on the enemy camp, and they were amazed at what they heard: that vast army was afraid of him and of his God! Some had had terrifying dreams of defeat and they were frightened. They had no idea, of course, that Gideon was reduced to three hundred men armed only with swords and trumpets.

Gideon and Purah returned to the Israelite camp and woke the pathetically small army. Gideon divided the three hundred men into three companies; he placed trumpets and empty jars in the hands of all of them, then torches were placed inside the jars. "Watch me," Gideon told them. "Follow my lead. When I get to the edge of the camp, do exactly as I do. When I and all who are with me blow our trumpets, then from all around the camp blow yours and shout, 'For the Lord and for Gideon.' "

Gideon and his company of one hundred men reached the edge of the camp at the beginning of the middle watch, just after they had changed the guard. They blew their trumpets and broke the jars that were in their hands. All three companies blew their trumpets and smashed their jars. With torches in their left hands, and trumpets in their right hands, they blew the trumpets and shouted, "A sword for the Lord and for Gideon."

The camp was thrown into utter chaos. Three hundred trumpets blasting out in the darkness was enough to send the enemy running in circles, turning on each other with their swords. It was a complete rout. A self-inflicted massacre. A great triumph for Gideon, the mighty warrior, and his God.

But you can't please all the people all the time, and there were some who were definitely not pleased. Gideon and his three hundred men were exhausted, but they continued in pursuit of the enemy to the other side of the River Jordan. Gideon pleaded with the men of Succoth to give him and his troops some bread. "They are worn out," he said, "and I am still pursuing Zebah and Zalmunna, the kings of Midian."

But because they didn't consider the war won without the capture of the kings, and because they thought little of Gideon, an upstart from the half-tribe of Manasseh, the men of Succoth refused Gideon and his men food. Gideon stayed there just long enough to give fair warning of what he intended for them on his return. Gideon said, **"Just for that, when the Lord has given Zebah and Zalmunna into my hand, I will tear your flesh with desert thorns (thistles) and briers.**

Gideon made the same request in Peniel, and they gave him the same answer. So he said to the men of Peniel, "When I return in triumph, I will tear down your tower."

Gideon caught the kings of Midian and on the way back with them he paid another visit to Succoth. **He took seventy-seven officials of that place, the elders of the town, and taught them a sharp lesson. He scourged them with thistles and briars.** He stopped off at Peniel too, pulled down the tower and killed the men of the town.

Gideon would have spared the Midianite kings, but they had killed two of his brothers and they taunted him, not thinking he had the stomach to kill them himself: "Come," said Zebah and Zalmunna, "Come, do it yourself. As is the man, so is his strength." So Gideon stepped forward and killed them, and took the ornaments off their camels' necks. He really had become a warrior of stature.

The Israelites wanted Gideon to rule over them, but he declined. "God will rule over you," he said. 'Thus Midian was subdued before the Israelites and did not raise its head again. During Gideon's lifetime, the land enjoyed peace for forty years.'

Barley ~ (*Hordeum species*)

Plant description

Barley is an annual of the Grass family, like wheat. Tall erect stalks bear distinctive ears of grain with long bristles. If it is 'two row barley' (*H. distichum*) it has just two rows of grains in each ear, whereas *H. hexastichum* bears six rows. Barley is an early crop, usually sown as 'winter barley'. It has a shorter growing season than wheat and will tolerate quite poor soil. It is not good for bread, but being low in gluten (unlike wheat) it can be used for unleavened bread, as forage and for a mulitiplicity of other purposes – not least of which is in the brewing and distilling industry. No wonder so many wayside hostelries are called 'The Barley Mow'! (A barley mow was a stook ready for collection after harvesting.) Barley used to be an ingredient of those wonderful travel sickness sweets, but now 'barley sugar' is simply a twist of amber-coloured sugar, untouched by the cereal which gives it its name.

Plant lore

In Tennyson's great love poem, 'The Lady of Shalott', the lady sees through her mirror as she sits at her loom:

> **On either side the river lie**
> **Long fields of barley and of rye,**
> **That clothe the wold and meet the sky;**
> **And through the field the road runs by**
> **To many-towered Camelot.**

and only the early reapers, 'in among the bearded barley', hear her song of longing.

Barley is one of the first crops on record. (It was grown in neolithic times – in the late Stone Age – when men were still using polished stone implements and weapons.)

Barley is mentioned more than thirty times in the Bible. Although it was considered an inferior crop to wheat, it had the advantage of growing in almost any conditions.

One spring in Galilee, a boy gave his picnic – five barley loaves and two small fish – and in return saw the great miracle of the feeding of the five thousand. (John 6:1-13). Inferior perhaps, but the great Roman statesman Pliny (AD23-79) referred to barley, and poets have written about Ruth, gleaning barley. Keats has her in tears 'amid the alien corn' in his 'Ode to a Nightingale'. But it is through the barley and its gleaning that Ruth finally finds fulfilment and happiness.

Uses in modern herbal medicine

Barley is rich in vitamins B and E and its action is demulcent, which has made it popular with the sick and the convalescent for many years. Barley water can be taken when copious fluids are prescribed and for nutrition when appetite is jaded. It is soothing to the bowel, reducing inflammation of the gut and relieving diarrhoea.

Barley was given to children in Britain during the Second World War in the form of malt extract, to provide essential vitamins and nutrition during a period of severe rationing.

Since an ingredient of the root of the germinating barley, Hordenine, is an alkaloid with similar properties to ephedrine, it can be useful in some allergic conditions, such as asthma. In these circumstances it has the advantage of fewer side-effects, such as over-stimulation of the nervous system.

'AMID THE ALIEN CORN'

This story, quite early on in the Bible, is very important, although at the time Ruth herself seemed of little or no account. She was not a Jewess, but a Moabitess – an alien, a gentile. Nevertheless, Ruth is later mentioned right at the beginning of St Matthew's Gospel in the genealogical list showing the ancestry of Jesus. (Matthew 1:1-17)

I was once asked to read the beginning of St Matthew's Gospel, and I asked if I should begin *after* the list of difficult names – beginning at Abraham and toiling through many generations before reaching our final destination: 'and Jacob fathered Joseph, the husband of Mary; of her was born Jesus, who is called Christ. Thus there were fourteen generations in all from Abraham to David, fourteen from David to the exile to Babylon, and fourteen from the exile to the Christ.'

I was told to read the whole thing; in fact, the homily was to be given not on the Annunciation or the Nativity, nor on the visit of the Magi bearing their gifts, but on the gentile women (four of them) who had played such major roles in the emergence of the Jewish nation. Ruth is there: '. . . **Boaz, the father of Obed, whose mother was Ruth, Obed the father of Jesse, and Jesse the father of King David.'**

The Book of Ruth is short – just four chapters sandwiched between the important books of Judges (21 chapters), which covers two centuries of Israel's early history-between the settlement in Canaan, the Promised Land, and the beginning of the monarchy in the first book of Samuel (31 chapters).

So why is it there at all? What is its significance in Israel's history? What has it to do with us in our journey with herbs?

Its opening is far from auspicious: 'In the days when the judges ruled, there was a famine in the land, and a man from Bethlehem in Judah, together with his wife and two sons, went to live for a while in the country of Moab. The man's name was Elimelech, his wife's name Naomi, and the names of his two sons were Mahlon and Kilion . . .'

They haven't been in Moab long before tragedy strikes. Elimelech dies, leaving Naomi with her two sons, who have married local women, one named Orpah and the other Ruth. But the sons die too and Naomi is left destitute.

By then the famine in Judah has eased, so Naomi decides to go back home. She tells her daughters-in-law to return to their families. "Go back, each of you, to your mother's home. May the Lord show kindness to you, as you have shown to your dead and to me. May the Lord grant that each of you will find rest in the home of another husband."

Orpah kisses Naomi goodbye, but Ruth clings to her: "Don't urge me to leave you or to turn back from you. Where you go I will go, and where you stay I will stay. Your people will be my people and your God my God. Where you die I will die, and there I will be buried. May the Lord deal with me, be it ever so severely, if anything but death separates you and me." Naomi argues against this, but when she realizes that Ruth is determined to go with her, she stops urging her:

'So the two women went on until they came to Bethlehem. (*Bethlehem means 'house of bread'*.) When they arrived the whole town was stirred because of them, and the women exclaimed, "Can this be Naomi?"

"Don't call me Naomi," she told them. "Call me Mara, because the Almighty has made my life very bitter. I went away full, but the Lord has brought me back empty . . ." Poor Naomi.

In the second chapter we read: 'Now Naomi had a relative on her husband's side . . . a man of standing whose name was Boaz.

'And Ruth . . . said to Naomi, "Let me go to the fields and pick up the left-over grain behind anyone in whose eyes I find favour. Naomi said to her, "Go ahead my daughter."

'So she went out and began to glean in the fields behind the harvesters. As it turned out, she found herself working in a field belonging to Boaz, who was from the clan of Elimelech.'

Boaz asks his foreman who she is, and he tells him about her, how she came from Moab with Naomi, how she has worked steadily all day, hardly resting. Boaz tells Ruth to stay in that field with his own servant girls. He has made sure his men don't trouble her, and when she gets thirsty she is to drink from the water jars the men have filled. Boaz tells Ruth that he has heard of her goodness to Naomi. At mealtime, Boaz invites her to join him, to take some bread and to dip it in the wine vinegar, and when she sits down with the harvesters, he offers her some roasted grain. Boaz instructs his men: "Even if she gathers among the sheaves, don't embarrass her. Rather, pull out some stalks for her from the bundles and leave them for her to pick up, and don't rebuke her."

'So Ruth gleaned in the field until evening. Then she threshed the barley she had gathered, and it amounted to about an ephah. She carried it back to town, and her mother- in law saw how much she had gathered. Ruth also brought out and gave her what she had left over after she had eaten enough.

'Her mother-in-law asked her: "Where did you glean today? Where did you work? Blessed be the man who took notice of you!"'

When Ruth told Naomi about Boaz, Naomi said, "It will be good for you, my daughter, to go with his girls, because in someone else's field you might be harmed."

'So Ruth stayed close to the servant girls of Boaz to glean until the barley and wheat harvests were finished. And she lived with her mother-in-law.'

Things are not moving quite quickly enough for Naomi and she decides to 'expedite' matters. She muses that Boaz is a kinsman and that he will be winnowing barley on the threshing floor. She tells Ruth to wash and put on perfume and dress in her best clothes. When Boaz has eaten and drunk and goes to lie down, Ruth is to go, uncover his feet and lie down. (In biblical terms this is a euphemism for slipping into bed with him, a sort of declaration of intent and quite a risky thing in the circumstances.)

Ruth obeys Naomi. In the middle of the night, Boaz becomes aware of a woman lying at his feet. Startled, he asks who it is, and she says, "I am your servant Ruth. Spread the corner of your garment over me since you are a kinsman redeemer."

Boaz knows that Ruth has not run after the younger men and he wants Ruth, but there is another kinsman redeemer in the equation, nearer even than Boaz is to Naomi, and by law his claim to Elimelech's inheritance has to be considered. In other words, Boaz's rival has to be offered first refusal.

This is an anxious time for both Ruth and Naomi. Boaz has fixed a meeting with the other kinsman redeemer and ten elders of the town to discuss the matter. Women are not included in such meetings. Ruth has no choice in the matter. She and Naomi can only wait at home and hope . . .

At the meeting, Boaz declares that Naomi is selling the piece of land that had belonged to her husband, and the kinsman redeemer agrees to redeem it. Then Boaz plays his highest card, practically holding his breath. He (Boaz) points out that in acquiring the land the other kinsman redeemer will also acquire the dead man's widow. To Boaz's relief, the other man says he can't, for fear of endangering his own estate. "You redeem it yourself," he says. "I cannot do it."

The writer of the Book of Ruth tells the story so beautifully that I don't want to change a word of the last chapter. We begin at verse seven:

(Now in earlier times in Israel, for the redemption and transfer of property to become final, one party took off his sandal and gave it to the other. This was the method of legalising transactions in Israel.) 'So the kinsman redeemer said to Boaz, "Buy it yourself." And he removed his sandal.

'Then Boaz announced to the elders and all the people, "Today you are witnesses that I have bought from Naomi all the property of Elimelech,

Kilion and Mahlon. I have also acquired Ruth the Moabitess, Mahlon's widow, as my wife, in order to maintain the name of the dead with his property, so that his name will not disappear from among his family or from the town records. Today you are witnesses!"

'Then the elders and all those at the gate said, "We are witnesses. May the Lord make the woman who is coming into your home like Rachel and Leah, who together built up the house of Israel. May you have standing in Ephrathah and be famous in Bethlehem.

'Through the offspring the Lord gives you by this young woman, may your family be like that of Perez, whom Tamar bore to Judah."

'So Boaz took Ruth and she became his wife. Then he went to her, and the Lord enabled her to conceive, and she gave birth to a son.

'The women said to Naomi: "Praise be to the Lord, who this day has not left you without a kinsman redeemer. May he become famous throughout Israel.

'He will renew you in your old age. For your daughter-in-law, who loves you and who is better to you than seven sons, has given him birth.

'Then Naomi took the child, laid him in her lap and cared for him. The women living there said, "Naomi has a son." And they named him Obed. He was the father of Jesse, the father of David.'

Terebinth ~ (*Pistacia terebinthus*)

Plant description

Ratcliffe says that most biblical scholars believe many trees mentioned are in fact terebinth and not oak . . . 'The terebinth is a large, deciduous tree with a short trunk and spreading, thick, ragged and twisted branches that lack symmetry. It has nasty, dead boughs, some of which hang low, ready to snare the unwary who dares pass under its canopy . . . Although the timber of the tree was of little use for building, the short, twisted lengths of hard wood were ideal for carving out idols. The tree was, and probably still is, the source of the product 'cyprus turpentine'. During the summer months the bark of the tree would be incised in several places to yield a very sticky, transparent fluid. The fluid would go through various cleansing processes to prepare it for marketing as 'purified cyprus turpentine'.

Zohary says that the Hebrew *allon* in the Bible should be translated 'oak', while elah should be rendered as 'terebinth tree' and that this distinction has not always been strictly observed by translators.

Plant lore

We explored both evergreen oak (the Holm Oak) and the deciduous oak with the story of Abraham at Mamre back in Genesis. But the confusion in translation between 'oak' and 'terebinth' on other occasions in the Bible gives me an excuse to tell the story of King David and his son, Absalom. Unlike the 'stag oak', whose dead branches are carried at the crown of the tree, like antlers, the terebinth has wicked dead branches much lower down . . .

DAVID AND ABSALOM

Samuel was the last of the Judges of Israel. He had struggled to keep perverse Israel faithful to God, but it was an uphill and thankless task. When Samuel grew too old to cope any longer, he appointed his sons, Joel and Abijah as judges in his place, 'But his sons did not walk in his ways. They turned aside after dishonest gain and accepted bribes and perverted justice.' (I Samuel 8:3) So the elders and the people demanded a king to lead them, like all the other nations. Samuel wasn't best pleased about this and he went to talk to the Lord about it. The Lord wasn't too keen on the idea either, but he told Samuel what to tell the people:

'Samuel told all the words of the Lord to the people who were asking him for a king. He said, "This is what the king who will reign over you will do: He will take your sons and make them serve with his chariots and horses, and they will run in front of his chariots. Some he will assign to be commanders of thousands and commanders of fifties, and others to plough his ground and reap his harvest, and still others to make weapons of war and equipment for his chariots. He will take your daughters to be perfumers and cooks and bakers. He will take the best of your fields and vineyards and olive groves and give them to his attendants. He will take a tenth of your grain and of your vintage and give it to his officials and attendants. Your menservants and maidservants and the best of your cattle and donkeys he will take for his own use. He will take a tenth of your flocks, and you yourselves will become his slaves. When that day comes, you will cry out for relief from the king you have chosen, and the Lord will not answer you in that day."

'But the people refused to listen to Samuel. "No!" they said. "We want a king over us. Then we shall be like all the other nations, with a king to lead us and to go out before us and fight our battles."

'When Samuel heard all that the people said, he repeated it before the Lord. The Lord answered, "Listen to them and give them a king."'

And so Israel got their first king. Saul started off with the best of intentions, but he had an unpredictable temper, frequent bouts of deep depression, and was capable of murderous hatred born out of jealousy (which was mostly directed towards David who would become Israel's ruler in its period of greatest glory and whose line led straight down to Jesus, the long-awaited Messiah).

David was the shepherd boy who killed the giant, Goliath, with a single stone from his sling. David was a fine musician (he wrote many of the psalms) who was employed at court to play and to sing, to soothe Saul in his black moods. David married Michal, Saul's youngest daughter, so he became 'family', and Jonathan, Saul's son, was David's close friend. But because David was popular with the people, Saul spent a lot of time and energy hating him and actually trying to kill him.

In the last chapter of the first book of Samuel, Saul's three sons (including Jonathan) were killed in one of the many battles against the Philistines and Saul himself was mortally wounded. To prevent capture and the abuse and humiliation that would inevitably follow, Saul killed himself with his own sword.

A messenger, a survivor from Saul's camp, managed to retrieve Saul's crown; he brought it to David with the news, and David mourned. (See David's lament for Saul and Jonathan in II Samuel 1:19-27).

David was now king. He could have kept everything gained from Saul for himself, but out of his love for his dead friend, Jonathan, he sought out a son, Mephibosheth, crippled in both feet when his nurse dropped him in infancy. So Saul's inheritance was given to Jonathan's son. 'And Mephibosheth lived in Jerusalem because he always sat at the king's table, and he was crippled in both feet.'

David is a strange mixture, and his story needs to be read straight from the Bible to get the full complexity of his personality. He is certainly not perfect. He not only commits adultery with Bathsheba, but puts Uriah, her husband, in the firing line in battle so that he will be killed when Bathsheba is found to be carrying David's child. The alliance produces a son, who dies soon after birth, but when David and Bathsheba are properly married, they produce Solomon, who will be the wisest man on earth and who will build God's Temple in Jerusalem.

David is not too fortunate with his sons. Amnon rapes Tamar (his half-sister) and Absalom orders his men to kill his brother, which they do. Absalom flees. David doesn't seem to have much difficulty in coming to terms with Amnon's death, but he misses Absalom and wants him home, but Absalom already has his eye on his father's throne and he hatches a conspiracy . . .

Perhaps we should take a closer look at Absalom before going any further, because the description of him in II Samuel 14:25-26 is relevant to our narrative:

'In all Israel there was not a man so highly praised for his handsome appearance as Absalom. From the top of his head to the sole of his foot there was no blemish in him. Whenever he cut the hair of his head – he used to cut his hair from time to time when it became too heavy for him – he would weigh it, and its

weight was two hundred shekels (about 5 pounds) by the royal standard.'

Back to the conspiracy. Absalom had ingratiated himself with the people; he had acquired horses and chariots and men; he had armed himself ready for a coup. Asked for his blessing for Absalom to go to Hebron, David gave it readily, but Absalom had sent messengers to all the tribes of Israel to say, "As soon as you hear the sound of the trumpets, then say, 'Absalom is king in Hebron.' "

David had to flee from Jerusalem, from Absalom, with his entire household, leaving only some reliable men behind to act as spies. There is a lot of intrigue and deception and there are stories within the main story, but eventually David mustered his troops and sent them out. He wanted to go with them, but was advised to stay and to support his army from the city.

'The king answered, "I will do whatever seems best to you." So the king stood beside the gate while all the men marched out . . .'

David was still concerned about his son: 'The king commanded Joab, Abishae and Ittai, "Be gentle with the young man, Absalom, for my sake." And all the troops heard the king giving orders concerning Absalom to each of the commanders.

'The army marched into the field to fight Israel, and the battle took place in the forest of Ephraim . . .' (II Samuel 18:3-6)

The main battle has taken place, David's army has won the day and there have been heavy casualties – but Absalom is not among them. Not yet.

'Now Absalom happened to meet David's men. He was riding his mule, and as the mule went under the thick branches of a large oak, Absalom's head got caught in the tree. He was left hanging in mid-air, while the mule he was riding kept on going.

'When one of the men saw this, he told Joab, "I have just seen Absalom hanging in an oak tree."

Joab went back and plunged three javelins into Absalom's heart, while Absalom was still alive. Then Absalom's body was taken down, thrown into a pit and covered with rocks.

No-one knew quite how to tell David of Absalom's death, but a messenger, a Cushite, was able to deliver the news in a roundabout way: 'The king asked the Cushite, "Is the young man Absalom safe?"

'The Cushite replied, "May the enemies of my lord the king and all who rise up to harm you be like that young man."

'The king was shaken. He went up to the room over the gateway and wept. As he went, he said: "O my son Absalom! My son, my son, Absalom! If only I had died instead of you – O Absalom, my son, my son!"

'Joab was told, "The king is weeping and mourning for Absalom." And for the whole army the victory that day was turned into mourning, because on that day the troops heard it and said, "The king is grieving for his son." The men stole into the city that day as men steal in who are ashamed when they flee from battle. The king covered his face and cried aloud, "O my son, Absalom! O Absalom, my son, my son!" '

The Vine ~ (*Vitis vinifera*)

Plant description

Zohary: 'The vine is a climbing shrub from whose base numerous slender branches sprout, straggling along the ground or climbing by means of long entwined tendrils. The plant simultaneously produces sterile and fertile branches, the latter growing so fast that they sometimes attain a length of two to four metres during a single season. Since they are too weak to support themselves and their heavy load of grapes, they are usually held up on sticks. The leaves, which are divided into five-toothed lobes, unfold in early spring and drop off late in summer. The minute, greenish flowers, in thickly branched clusters, shed their hood-like cover when they open. Pollination is induced by bees, which gather both pollen and nectar from the flowers. The fruit, whose colour comes from the membranous skin but whose flesh itself is colourless, is a berry containing two seeds in each of its two cells. In the wild species, the berries are dispersed by birds.'

Plant lore

As Tom Ratcliffe points out: 'The vast majority of trees and shrubs throughout the world have more than one pleasing and useful feature; such as decorative form, colourful flowers, fruits, foliar tints and timber for construction work or for burning to keep oneself warm. The vine, on the other hand, has no desirable symmetry in its form of growth; its flowers are green and insignificant; the foliage has no seasonal beauty and its timber is of no commercial value. Indeed, the wood burns so quickly when fired that it provides very little warmth . . . The singular and most valued attribute of the vine is its fruit.'

This echoes Ezekiel (Chapter 15) when God speaks of Jerusalem being a useless vine . . . **"Son of man, how is the wood of the vine better than that of a branch on any of the trees in the forest? Is wood ever taken from it to make anything useful? Do they make pegs from it to hang things on? And after it is thrown on the fire as fuel and the fire burns both ends and chars the middle, is it then useful for anything? If it was not useful for anything when it was whole, how much less can it be made into something useful when the fire has burned it and it is charred?"**

One attribute only, but what an attribute! In the Book of Numbers (Chapter 13), we read that the spies returning from reconnaissance in the Promised Land, came back staggering under the weight of a pole on which was carried a single branch of grapes, some pomegranates and some figs. They called the place Eshcol, which means 'cluster', so the Israelites waiting back at base camp were obviously impressed with such fecundity.

The vine was to the Israelites an image of God's bounty and blessing, and the vine is often paired with the fig tree in this respect. The vine was their national emblem. It appeared as decoration on mosaic floors and over the doors of synagogues; it was carved on furniture, painted on murals, stamped on coins. Even in captivity and exile, the Israelites chiselled the vine on tombstones in hostile and alien lands. At the time of grape harvest - in the vintage season - there would be great celebration. In Genesis (Chapter 49), Jacob (who has been re-named 'Israel'), receives God's blessing: **'He will tether his donkey to a vine, his colt to the choisest branch; he will wash his garments in wine, his robes in the blood of grapes.'** Well, that's God for you, he never does anything by halves; always lavish to a fault.

There is a lovely passage in Deuteronomy (Chapter 8): **'Observe the commands of the Lord your God, walking in his ways and revering him. For the Lord your God is bringing you into a good land – a land with streams and pools of water, with springs flowing in the valleys and hills; a land with wheat and barley, vines and fig trees, pomegranates, olive oil and honey; a land where bread will not be scarce and you will lack nothing; a land where rocks are iron and you can dig copper out of the hills. When you have eaten and are satisfied, praise the Lord your God for the good land he has given you.'**

And, of course, St John's Gospel, Chapter 15, in which Jesus tells the Parable of the Vine. Jesus is the true vine and his Father is the gardener, removing barren branches and pruning those that are productive so that they fruit even more abundantly.

We could go on indefinitely. The importance of viticulture in biblical times is incalculable. It was the symbol of peace and prosperity. Every man's dream, and God's promise to his people, was that he should possess his own vine and sit in the shade of his own fig tree. So, when God was displeased with the Israelites and told them so through his prophets, the blessing of the vine is turned into more of a curse. Isaiah prophesied (Chapter 16): **'Joy and gladness are taken away from the orchards; no-one sings or shouts in the vineyards; no-one treads out wine at the presses, for I have put an end to shouting.'**

In Greek mythology, the ancients extolled the virtue of wine with Bacchus in revellry and symposia (Bacchus, translated from the Greek, means 'god of wine'), but it was probably the effect of the alcohol rather than other virtues of wine being celebrated

Uses in modern herbal medicines

During the latter part of the 20th century, an intense level of research was undertaken into the causes and prevention of heart disease. This research resulted in much speculation as to why the populations of Italy and France have a lower mortality rate from heart and circulatory disease than other European populations, although they consume much the same quantities of saturated fats in their diets. When their penchant for fine wines came under scrutiny, it was discovered that red wines contain compounds (poly-phenols) that provide protection from arterio-sclerotic disease. It was adjudged that these factors in such wines played a major role in reducing the levels of heart attack and stroke in the French and the Italians. Doctors and nutritionists in the UK are now advising that moderate drinking of red wine is an excellent way of preventing heart disease, and this message is being received gladly by their patients. There always has to be a word of caution; due to the adverse effects of alcohol, just one glass (125ml) of red wine a day is recommended. Sorry!

NABOTH'S VINEYARD

With no preamble and no introduction, 'Elijah the Tishbite, from Tishbe in Gilead, said to Ahab, "As the Lord, the God of Israel, lives, whom I serve, there will be neither dew nor rain in the next few years except at my word." (1 Kings 17:1)

We are never much the wiser about Elijah's background, but we know all about Ahab. He (Ahab) has just succeeded to the throne of Israel, following in the footsteps of a whole bunch of terrible kings. Ahab is not an improvement: 'In the thirty-eighth year of Asa, King of Judah, Ahab, son of Omri, became king over Israel, and he reigned in Samaria over Israel for twenty-two years. Ahab son of Omri did more evil in the sight of the Lord than any of those before him. He not only considered it trivial to commit the sins of Jeroboam son of Nebat, but he also married Jezebel, daughter of Ethbaal, king of the Sidonians, and began to serve Baal and worship him.'

There are no adequate words to describe Jezebel. Virago gets nowhere near it. Ahab might have been wicked, but he was a wimp compared to his wife. But, more of her later. . .

And so, Elijah appears. He just leaps on to centre stage, delivers his message from God and (following sound advice from God) makes a very hasty retreat. God has made some rather good arrangements for Elijah: his prophet must go and hide in the Kerith Ravine, east of the Jordan River. There is a convenient brook to supply him with water and he is to be fed bread and meat by ravens. So far so good, but of course there is a drought and the brook dries up.

Elijah is then instructed to go to Zarephath in Sidon, where a widow will feed him. Elijah goes to Zarephath and he finds the widow easily enough, gathering sticks near the well. She gives Elijah a drink, but says there is nothing to eat; she and her son are just about to have their last meal before they die, the flour and oil having run out. Of course, God performs a miracle through Elijah so that the flour and oil never run out again and Elijah stays in Zarephath for three years – until God tells him to go and present himself to Ahab to tell him that it is going to rain.

Bearing the good news of the end of the drought, Elijah is not killed on sight, but the welcome is not warm: "Is that you, you troubler of Israel?" Ahab asks. At this point Elijah is quite confident, having received specific instructions from God. He tells Ahab to summon all the Israelites to meet him on Mount Carmel, plus the 450 prophets of Baal and the 400 prophets of Asherah, who are favourites of Jezebel, and this is done. There follows a wonderful competition. Elijah invites all these worshippers of false gods to offer sacrifice and to pray down fire.

The prophets of Baal and of Asherah are hard at it for most of the day, shouting and dancing around their altar. Elijah taunts them, until they get into a frenzy and cut themselves until blood flows. There is no answer.

In the evening, Elijah prepares his altar with its sacrifice and pours water on to the sacrifice and the altar until it runs down into the trench; then Elijah prays that God will show them all that there is a God in Israel. 'Then the fire of the Lord fell and burned up the sacrifice, the wood, the stones and the soil, and also licked up the water in the trench. When all the people saw this they fell prostrate and cried, "The Lord – he is God! The Lord – he is God!" Then Elijah commands the people to seize the false prophets and kill them, which they do.

The rain starts and Ahab rides off to Jezreel. Elijah is so cock-a-hoop that he tucks his cloak into his belt and runs ahead of Ahab all the way to Jezreel.

When Ahab tells Jezebel everything that has happened she is furious and Elijah has to run for his life, into the Judean desert. He sits under a broom tree and prays for death. Then he falls asleep . . .

Actually, he hasn't done at all badly, but he is exhausted and out of adrenaline and he falls asleep. Soon, along comes an angel and bakes him some bread over hot coals and gives him a nice jug of cool water. Elijah eats and drinks and goes back to sleep. Again the angel comes and he eats and drinks again. This time he feels sufficiently refreshed to travel for forty days and nights until he reaches Horeb, the mountain of God, where he goes into a cave to spend the night.

In the morning God asks him what he is doing there, and Elijah is again in whining mode: "I am the only one left and now they are trying to kill me too," he says. God is about to show Elijah a thing or two; he tells Elijah to go out and stand on the mountain, "For the Lord is about to pass by."

'Then a great and powerful wind tore the mountains apart and shattered the rocks before the Lord, but the Lord was not in the wind. After the wind there was an earthquake, but the Lord was not in the earthquake. After the earthquake came a fire, but the Lord was not in the fire. And after the fire came a gentle whisper. When Elijah heard it, he pulled his cloak over his face and went out and stood at the mouth of the cave.

'Then a voice said to him, "What are you doing here, Elijah?"

Poor Elijah gives the same answer, but, one imagines, in a very different tone of voice. He is told to go back the way he came and to anoint a few future kings and prophets.

It is time we got to Naboth's vineyard (1 Kings, Chapter 21).

Naboth's vineyard was in Jezreel, close to Ahab's palace. Ahab asked Naboth to let him have the vineyard to use as a vegetable garden, because of its proximity to the palace. He offered Naboth another, better vineyard, or, if he preferred, the price of the vineyard, but Naboth refused, saying, "The Lord forbid that I should give you the inheritance of my fathers."

That really was not a very wise move on Naboth's part. Ahab went home, sullen and angry; he lay on his bed sulking and he refused to eat. When Jezebel asked what was the matter, Ahab recounted the story of his encounter with Naboth. Jezebel's reaction to her childish, petulant husband was predictable: "Is this how you act as king over Israel? Get up and eat! I'll get you the vineyard of Naboth the Jezreelite." And so she did, by getting some scoundrels to testify against him that he had cursed both God and the king. Consequently Naboth was stoned to death.

Ahab acquired Naboth's vineyard, but he didn't enjoy it for long. Elijah was sent to Ahab and gave such a terrifying prophesy of disaster to him and his house (including the eating of Jezebel by dogs) that 'When Ahab heard these words, he tore his clothes, put on sackcloth and fasted. He lay in sackcloth and went around meekly.'

Because Ahab humbled himself, God relented. Ahab was eventually killed in battle, but much later (2 Kings 9). Jezebel was thrown out of a window, where she was trampled by horses and eaten by dogs so that only her skull, hands and feet were left.

Elijah went on to lead a most interesting life. He didn't die, but was taken up into the sky in a chariot, while his prophet's mantle fell on Elisha, his anointed successor.

4 | The Books of Chronicles

Why bother with the books of Chronicles when the books of 2 Samuel and 1 and 2 Kings tell of the same events and are so much more exciting? Why choose to read a highly moral history, when one can get a much more 'tabloid' and easily readable edition of the lives of the same kings and their times? And anyway, the first nine chapters are simply lists of names (except the gem of the prayer of Jabez in Chr 4:9-10, which looks as if the historian has put down his quill, gone off for a cup of coffee and someone has come along and inserted those two verses).

The answer has to be: because the books of Chronicles are important. The author has a definite purpose and a definite message. He gives a re-interpretation of the period from the death of Saul, through David's long reign to the end of the monarchy when the Israelites were carried off to exile in Babylon. This chronicler is concerned with worship of Yahweh, the holiness of the God of Israel, and the fidelity of kings and priests and people to that God. He is not going to spend time gossiping about the salacious: (David's adultery and intrigues, Solomon's harem and so on). Prayer and Temple worship is paramount here.

The material in the books of Chronicles was not new at the time of writing. Readers would have been familiar with the stories in Samuel and Kings so that the chronicler was free to write a much more focused work on his main themes.

This chronicler is writing for those who returned from exile in Babylon to rebuild Jerusalem under Ezra, who was '. . . a teacher well versed in the Law of Moses, which the Lord, the God of Israel had given.' Artaxerxes, king of Persia, 'granted him everything he asked, for the hand of the Lord his God was upon him . . . For Ezra had devoted himself to the study and observance of the Law of the Lord, and to teaching its decrees and laws in Israel.' (Ezra 7:1-10); and Nehemiah, who had been cup-bearer to Artaxerxes and who had begged to be released from service to go and rebuild his devastated city, Jerusalem, and had been given permission to go. (Nehemiah, Chapters 1-2).

The story of the good king Hezekiah, is told in both 2 Kings 18-20 and in 2 Chronicles 32, so that in the telling of it we shall be flitting from one to the other, but I think it well worth the trouble . . .

Fig ~ (*Ficus carica*)

Plant description

The fig tree is of moderate size, rarely reaching more than 5m in height, bushy and with a wide, shady spread, its lower branches quite close to the ground. The large, deeply lobed, glossy green leaves are quite distinctive and the trunk is a smooth, pale grey. The fig tree is deciduous, and in winter it is heartening to see bare twigs bearing green terminal buds, ready for spring.

Flowering of the fig is unusual: hundreds of star-shaped, translucent, white female flowers grow on the inside of the syconium – the hollow, fleshy receptacle that will eventually develop into the mature fruit – while male flowers grow near the ostium – the narrow opening at the 'neck' of the potential fruit.

Pollination is by means of a tiny gall wasp (*Blastophagia psenes*) which lays its eggs in short-styled female flowers and, in the process, pollinates other longer-styled flowers, which mature and cause the fig to ripen and swell into the familiar purple-brown fruit.

Plant lore

The fig played an important part in biblical times, both from the nutritional point of view, and as a powerful symbol. Its high sugar content meant that it could be dried, pressed and stored for long periods, and it was useful in this state against times when little other fruit was available, for taking on a journey or as a gift.

The fig tree itself was a symbol of peace and prosperity in the Old Testament. In Zechariah, chapter 3, the prophet promises: **'In that day each of you will invite his neighbour to sit under his vine and fig-tree, declares the Lord Almighty.'**

The fig was a sign of spring in the Lover's passionate invitation to his Beloved (Song of Songs Ch 2:11-13):

> "See! The winter is past;
> the rains are over and gone.
> Flowers appear on the earth;
> the season of singing has come,
> the cooing of doves is heard in our land.

The fig tree forms its early fruit;
The blossoming vines spread their fragrance.
Arise, come, my darling;
    my beautiful one, come with me."

And, of course, the fig tree was there at the tragedy of the Garden of Eden: 'When the woman saw that the fruit of the tree was good for food and pleasing to the eye, and also desirable for gaining wisdom, she took some and ate it. She also gave some to her husband who was with her, and he ate it. Then the eyes of both of them were opened, and they realised that they were naked; **so they sewed fig leaves together and made coverings for themselves.'**

There is nothing sadder in all Scripture than the moment when God comes into the garden at cool of day to meet Adam and Eve, only to find that they have hidden from him in shame. His call "Where are you?" echoes down the years and the Creator of Adam and Eve and their paradise garden probably weeps as he asks them: "Who told you that you were naked? Have you eaten from the tree from which I commanded you not to eat?" (Genesis 3:6-11)

Apparently, Fig Sunday was another name for Palm Sunday in some places. Figs were eaten on that day to commemorate the blasting of the barren fig-tree by Jesus. (Mark 11:12-14 and 20-21). One legend has it that Judas Iscariot hanged himself on a fig tree; another that Jesus' Cross was of fig wood.

The fig is part of Jesus' promise to the disciples when he is talking about the 'end times' when he will come again. He tells them what signs to look for as the time approaches and he compares them to those of the fig: **"Now learn this lesson from the fig-tree: As soon as its twigs get tender and its leaves come out, you know that summer is near."**

In medieval England, the fig was regarded as a 'cure-all'. Warts, scurf, scabs, running sores, bruises, toothache, deafness and tinnitus, coughs, hoarseness, any disease of the chest or lungs, dropsy, the bloody flux, falling-sickness and whatever else ailed anyone. However, since figs had to be imported from the Middle East or the Mediterranean they wouldn't have been available for most people.

Uses in modern herbal medicine

We are all familiar with figs for breakfast, or as one of the delicious ingredients of a fruit compôte, but figs are an excellent laxative, having the advantage of a gentle, demulcent action so that Syrup of Figs can be used for children and the elderly and for anyone who is mildly 'costive'. Syrup of Figs has been a standard herbal medicine for the treatment of constipation for many years and it is included in the current *British Pharmacopoeia.*

Some people still swear by the (external) application of the 'milk' of the fig – the juice from leaves or branches – for removing warts; and the soft inner pulp of cooked figs can be used as a poultice to boils and carbuncles. Which brings me neatly to:

A POULTICE FIT FOR A KING

Hezekiah was 25 years old when he became King of Judah (*c*700BC) and he ruled for 29 years. After a succession of bad kings who had led the people to break their covenant with God, Hezekiah was good, and his goodness was coupled with tremendous energy. First of all he tore down all the idols to strange gods that his people had been worshipping, then he cleansed the Temple, reconsecrated it and called the priests and the people to re-dedicate themselves to the Lord. A proclamation was sent out to all Israel 'from Beersheba to Dan' calling the people to go to Jerusalem to celebrate Passover together.

King Hezekiah repaired broken sections of the city wall and built watchtowers on it. He built another wall outside the old wall and re-inforced the terraces.

'This is what Hezekiah did thoughout Judah, doing what was good and right and faithful before the Lord his God. In everything that he undertook in the service of God's temple and in obedience to the law and the commands, he sought his God and worked wholeheartedly. And so he prospered.' (2 Chronicles 31:20-21)

'Hezekiah trusted in the Lord, the God of Israel. There was no-one like him among all the kings of Judah, either before him or after him. He held fast to the Lord and did not cease to follow him; he kept the commands the Lord had given Moses. And the Lord was with him; he was successful in whatever he undertook. He rebelled against the king of Assyria and did not serve him. From watchtower to fortified city, he defeated the Philistines as far as Gaza and its territory.' (2 Kings Chapter 18).

As well as religious reform, Hezekiah set about improving political and military capacities in the nation. He greatly increased his stock of armaments. He ordered a watercourse to be built into Jerusalem by diverting water from springs and streams outside the city. He was a splendid new broom in the throne-room. But there was a huge cloud on the horizon in the shape of Sennacherib, the king of Assyria with his vast army.

Even before Jerusalem was attacked, the mere threat from mighty Assyria slowly strangled the little kingdom of Judah. Hezekiah tried to buy his way out of trouble, tried to buy peace for his people in whatever coin Sennacherib demanded. Hezekiah gradually emptied the treasury, spent all his reserves, stripped the Temple of anything of value and the kingdom of Judah became bankrupt in the face of invaders.

Jerusalem was besieged, but managed to hold out because of Hezekiah's forethought in providing a water supply into the city. The people were hungry and afraid and they wanted to surrender to Sennacherib, but Hezekiah was wise enough to consult God's prophet, Isaiah. Isaiah and Hezekiah prayed together:

'King Hezekiah and the prophet Isaiah, son of Amoz cried out in prayer to heaven about this. And the Lord sent an angel, who annihilated all the fighting men and the leaders and officers in the camp of the Assyrian king. So he (Sennacherib) withdrew to his own land in disgrace. And when he went into the temple of his god, some of his sons cut him down with the sword.

'So the Lord saved Hezekiah and the people of Jerusalem from the hand of Sennacherib, king of Assyria, and from the hand of all the others. He took care of them on every side. Many brought offerings to Jerusalem for the Lord and valuable gifts for Hezekiah, king of Judah. From then on he was highly regarded by all the nations.' (2 Chronicles 32:20-23).

'Hezekiah had very great riches and honour, and he made treasuries for his silver and gold and for his precious stones, spices, shields and all kinds of valuables. He also made buildings to store the harvest of grain, new wine and oil; and he made stalls for various kinds of cattle, and pens for the flocks. He built villages and acquired great numbers of flocks and herds, for God had given him very great riches.' (2 Chronicles 32:27-29).

That would seem a good place to end Hezekiah's story, but it isn't finished quite yet. Hezekiah was as human as the next man, and no man is perfect. All the success and acclaim went to his head and he forgot to give the glory to God. He began to believe that all the miracles had been his own doing. His sin was pride. Hezekiah was ill, very ill indeed, at the point of death, when his old friend, the prophet Isaiah, went to see the king. Isaiah had a short sharp message from God for Hezekiah: "This is what the Lord says: Put your house in order, because you are going to die; you will not recover." Hezekiah turned his face to the wall and prayed to the Lord . . . And Hezekiah wept bitterly.' (2 Kings 20:1-2)

But Isaiah hadn't left the king's palace before he had another message from God. Isaiah was to go back and tell Hezekiah that his prayer had been heard, his tears seen, and that God would heal him. So Isaiah hurried back with the good news. Isaiah instructed the servants: **"Prepare a poultice of figs ." They did so and applied it to the boil, and Hezekiah recovered.** (2 Kings 20:7)

Hezekiah lived for the next 15 years, as God had promised he would. We are not told of the cause of his death, just that 'he rested with his fathers'. He was succeeded by his son, Manasseh, which was very bad news for the kingdom of Judah. (2 Kings Chapter 21)

5 | The Apocrypha
(*Deuterocanonical Books*)

Thirty-nine books of Hebrew Scripture form the basis of what we know as the 'Old Testament', but there has always been argument about the status of fifteen other books which form a varied collection of Jewish literature dating from about 300BC to 100AD. Although originally written in Hebrew, they have never been accepted as part of Jewish sacred Scripture.

For this reason St Jerome, priest and doctor of the Church – whose scholarship was unparalled in his time (c342-420AD) – argued against the authority of these books, although he agreed that they were valuable enough to be read in church. It was Jerome who first used the word 'Apocrypha' (in Greek it means 'hidden') to describe the nature of the book of Second Esdras (Fourth Esdras in Catholic Bibles) which contains 'hidden' mysteries given by God to Ezra, and thereby named the whole section of 'secondary' books.

Until recent years these books did not appear in any Bibles (except for seven of them – Tobit; Judith; The Book of Wisdom; Ecclesiasticus; the two books of Maccabees and Baruch- which have always been part of Catholic Scripture). Luther, in producing his Bible of 1534, plucked the apocryphal books from their usual places in the Old Testament and relegated them to the back of the Book with the somewhat dismissive legend: '*Apocrypha: these are books which are not held equal to the Sacred Scriptures and yet are useful and good for reading.*' For a time, printing apocryphal writings at the back of Protestant versions of the Bible was normal practice, but then they were omitted completely. Most Protestant Bibles still do not include them, but they can be obtained separately.

In Catholic Bibles, the additions to Esther are included in the Book of Esther; the Letter of Jeremiah comes in Baruch; and the Song of the Three Children, Susanna and Bel and the Dragon can be found in Daniel. The wonderful canticle/doxology, known as the *Benedicite:* 'O you works of the Lord, O bless the Lord. To him be highest glory and praise for ever . . .' comes in the addition to chapter 3 of Daniel with Shadrach, Meshach and Abed-Nego after their experience in the fiery furnace.

The Apocryphal books can be divided into sections: '**Historical**'; '**Religious Fiction**'; '**Wisdom**' and '**Apocalyptic**'.

In the 'Historical Section' we find **Esdras** (Ezra). There is an overlap with material in other books, but its primary addition to our knowledge of biblical events is the debate of the three young men (1 Esdras 3-4) which explains how Zerubbabel managed to extract permission from the Persian king (Artaxerxes) to rebuild the Temple in Jerusalem after the Babylonian exile.

1 and 2 Maccabees cover much the same material but are written from different points of view. In the first book we have the story of the Maccabean revolt against a foreign (Greek) culture. The second book is written in the form of a letter: 'The Jews in Jerusalem and those in the land of Judea, To their Jewish kindred in Egypt, Greetings and true peace . . .' and it takes a much more moralistic tone in telling about events.

Under 'Religious Fiction' comes **Tobit**, a story of perseverance and reward. I love Tobit because it is here we meet the Archangel Raphael – The Healer (in disguise, of course!), who restores Tobit's sight and keeps his son, Tobias, from harm.

Judith is a formidable heroine who uses all her (considerable) wiles to lure the enemy to death.

Additions to the Book of **Esther** attempt to introduce 'religion' into a book that is beautiful and worthy of inclusion in the Old Testament without ever actually mentioning God.

Additions to **Daniel** are further legends about the sage who was carried off into exile in Babylon and who found favour by telling the king the meaning of his dreams.

Wisdom literature in the Apocrypha is represented principally by Ecclesiasticus and The Wisdom of Solomon.

Ecclesiasticus (Sirach), dates from between 190 and 180BC This scribe of Jerusalem writes of the things he loves: Temple liturgy and the

Law. Wisdom comes from God, through the Law. The advice/reflections of Ben Sira are very much like those of Proverbs. Of relationships, he writes: 'Do not desert an old friend; the new one will not be his match. New friend, new wine; when it grows old, you drink it with pleasure.'

The Book of Wisdom (sometimes called The Wisdom of Solomon) was written about 50BC by a Jew who was thoroughly familiar with Greek culture. It was not written by King Solomon. Here, Wisdom is God's emissary, and again the book takes the same form as 'Proverbs'. For example: 'For the hope of the godless is like chaff carried on the wind, like fine spray driven by the storm; it disperses like smoke before the wind, goes away like the memory of a one-day guest.' (Wisdom 5:14 NJB)

The Book of Baruch is attributed to Jeremiah's secretary, but it was probably written much later. In Baruch we find expressed, in poetry and prose, the penitence and hope of the Jews in exile in Babylon. They remind God of all the wonders he performed for them in the past and plead with him for forgiveness and restoration to his favour until, in the last chapter they feel confident enough to praise him for what he will do for them.

The Letter of Jeremiah takes the form of a letter to those about to be carried off into exile, warning them not to worship foreign gods in captivity: 'Their wooden gods overlaid with gold and silver are like a scarecrow in a field of cucumbers – protecting nothing.'

The Prayer of Manasseh is one of penitence and trust in God's mercy.

2 Esdras is the only example of apocalyptic writing in the Apocrypha, featuring some prophetic visions ascribed to Ezra.

The Hebrew Bible as Jesus knew it was the Old Testament of 39 books. There are those who think the apocrypha has no place in the Bible at all; and those who do regard it as Scripture would concede that its 'authority' is of secondary importance to the original 39 books. Even so, much of it is beautiful and deeply spiritual and, as Luther said, '. . . they are useful and good for reading.'

Date Palm ~ (*Phoenix dactylifera*)

Plant description

Palm trees are unmistakable, growing up to 20m in height, the leaves themselves being several metres long with narrow, dark green leaflets arranged in pairs. The straight, branchless stems (trunks) are fibrous rather than woody, consisting mainly of old leaf bases which have broken off leaving a distinctive knobbled pattern, while the new, deciduous leaves are carried at the very top of the tree.

Palms are dioecious (female and male flowers borne on different plants), their blossom hanging in huge clusters at the top of the tree beneath the leaves. The date itself is a dark oval, single-stoned 'berry' which will only come to full maturity in a hot climate. Propagation is usually by using the suckers which sprout from the base of the stem so that the sex of the tree can be assured (far fewer males being required since they can each produce enough pollen to fertilize a large number of females) and so that the cultivated crop is kept genetically pure.

Date palms are native to Asia and North Africa. In cooler countries, palms are grown for ornamental purposes but will only produce immature, inedible fruit.

Plant lore

Like figs, dates have a high sugar content and lend themselves to drying, pressing and storing. The date palm is therefore a valuable food source in Middle Eastern countries.

The palm is also a tree that will flourish in an oasis. When the Israelites first escaped from captivity in Egypt they travelled in the desert for three whole days without water. Then they came to a place called Marah where there was water, but it was bitter and undrinkable. God showed Moses a piece of wood which, when thrown into the water made it sweet, so that they were able to drink and continue their journey. **'Then they came to Elim, where there were twelve springs and seventy palm trees, and they camped there near the water.'** (Exodus 15:27).

Deborah, a remarkable woman who was a judge in Israel at a time when women were not highly regarded (she was said to have *led* Israel), 'held court under the Palm of Deborah between Ramah and Bethel in the hill country of Ephraim, and the Israelites came to her to have their disputes decided.' (Judges 4:4-5)

The palm was a symbol of triumph and rejoicing. Its branches were waved at the Feast of Tabernacles, one of the seven great feasts set by God to be celebrated annually. (Leviticus 23)

Judith (we shall be meeting her a little later) carried pressed dates in her basket on her visit to Holofernes. And, of course, palm branches were laid before Jesus as he entered Jerusalem for Passover just before his death.

Uses in modern herbal medicine

Although the nutritional value of the date is high, and it has obvious advantages in storage and for out-of-season celebrations, it has no known medicinal use. However, because of its high sugar content it could be used as an antiseptic agent in an emergency and, like the fig, it could be used as a poultice for reducing local inflammation and for bringing boils to a head.

JUDITH'S PICNIC BASKET

*(This story comes from the Apocryphal Book of Judith in the
Old Testament and all quotations are taken from the New Jerusalem Bible)*

When Rudyard Kipling wrote his poem 'The Female of the Species', drawing graphic comparisons between male and female bears and cobras and wild Indians, and concluding at the end of each verse that the female of the species was more deadly than the male, he should have included Judith in his reckonings . . .

The Israelites were in trouble again. Unusually, this was not because they had turned away from God but because they were being obedient to him and refusing to worship alien gods.

Nebuchadnezzar, king of Assyria, who ruled from the great city of Nineveh and who was himself worshipped as a god, had conquered every nation that opposed him, with the help of the general in command of his army, a nasty piece of work called Holofernes.

The Assyrian army, including twelve thousand archers on horseback; a vast number of camels and donkeys and mules for transport; innumerable sheep and oxen and goats for food; ample rations for everyone; a huge amount of gold and silver from the royal palace; chariots, cavalry and infantry, set out ahead of the king with the intention of covering what they knew as 'the face of the whole earth'. With them went a mixed crowd, 'like a swarm of locusts, like the dust of the earth – a multitude that could not be counted.'

They marched for three days before they set camp, from where Holofernes took the whole army, ravaging and killing and plundering. He followed the Euphrates and passed through Mesopotamia, destroying all the fortified towns as far as the sea. He seized the territory of Cilicia; he went down into the plain of Damascus during the wheat harvest and burned the fields; he destroyed the flocks and herds, sacked the towns and put all the young men to the sword.

And so, as one can imagine, great fear and dread of Holofernes fell upon everyone in his path. Messengers were sent to him to sue for peace. They promised allegiance to Nebuchadnezzar, offering him their lands, their herds and flocks and the inhabitants of their towns as slaves. Reprieved, the people welcomed Holofernes and his army with garlands and music and dancing. Nevertheless, Holofernes destroyed all their shrines and their sacred groves and made the people worship King Nebuchadnezzar alone.

'Thus he reached the edge of Esdraelon, in the neighbourhood of Dothan, a village facing the great ridge of Judaea. He pitched his camp between Geba and Scythopolis and stayed there a full month to re-provision his forces.' (Judith Chaper 3:9-10)

When the Israelites living in Judea heard about everything Holofernes had done they were terrified. They had only recently returned from exile and their temple, its altar and all the sacred vessels had just been re-consecrated after their earlier desecration. They were fearful for themselves, for Jerusalem and for the temple of the Lord their God. So they immediately fortified the villages on the high hilltops and stored up food in preparation for a siege, which was made easier since their fields had recently been harvested.

Joakim, the high priest, ordered seizure of the mountain passes so that the enemy could be prevented from entering – again fortunate since the approach was narrow, wide enough for only two to pass at a time. Then the Israelites prayed with great fervour; they fasted; they covered themselves with sackcloth and put ashes on their heads; they even draped the temple altar with sackcloth, and they cried out to God to save them.

Holofernes heard that the Israelites were preparing for war. He knew they had closed the mountain passes and fortified the hilltops and set up barricades in the plains, and he was enraged. He called together the princes of Moab and the commanders of Ammon and all the governors of the coastland to ask them, '. . . tell me: what people is this that occupies the hill country? What towns does it inhabit? How large is its army? What are the sources of its power and strength? Who is the king who rules it and commands its army? Why have they disdained to wait on me, as all the western peoples have?'

Only one man dared answer Holofernes – Achior, the Ammonite leader. He told what he knew about the Israelites, how they worshipped the God of heaven, the God they had come to know, the God who had worked so many wonders for them. Achior said that as long as the Israelites did not sin against their God they prospered, because their God hated iniquity, but when they departed from the way he had prescribed for them they were utterly defeated in battle and were led away to a foreign land, their temple was razed to the ground and their towns were occupied by invading forces. They had returned to their God and were faithful to him; they had restored Jerusalem, their sacred city, and so God was faithful to them in return. Achior begged Holofernes to leave the people of Israel alone, for their God was bound to defend them and invaders would become the laughing-stock of the whole world.

Achior's report was not well received. Some suggested he be cut to pieces, but Holofernes ordered him to be bound, taken to the hill country near to one of the mountain passes, to await death along with the Israelites. However, the Israelites had posted watchmen who came down, untied him and treated him well. In return, Achior told them what had taken place in Holofernes' council and of his boasts about what he intended to do to the House of Israel.

Holofernes broke camp and moved his vast army to seize the passes up into the hill country. There were so many men – one hundred and seventy thousand infantry and twelve thousand cavalry, not counting the baggage and the foot-soldiers handling it, that the Israelites were terrified. Holofernes led out all his cavalry in full view of the Israelites. He seized the springs that supplied their water; he set guards over them and the rest of the army camped in the plain, covering the whole land.

The Israelites were surrounded; there was no way of escape. After thirty-four days all the water containers were empty, their cisterns were almost dry, water was rationed and people were collapsing from thirst. God seemed deaf to their cries.

Then the people began to demand surrender. They said it would be better to be captives and slaves than to watch their children die of thirst. The people were persuaded to wait for a few more days, but they were in great misery.

Enter Judith (whose name means simply 'The Jewess'), a beautiful young widow left very comfortably off by her husband, Manasseh. After her husband died, Judith had put sackcloth around her waist and dressed in widows' clothes; she managed her late husband's estate well, his men and women slaves, livestock and land. No-one spoke ill of Judith, for she feared God with great devotion.

When Judith heard about the proposed surrender, she spoke to the elders of her town. She accused them of putting God to the test. She reminded them that they had promised never to worship alien gods and that to become slaves again would dishonour them and God. Judith really laid it on the line. She said to the elders, 'Listen to me; I intend to do something, the memory of which will be handed down to the children of our race from age to age. Tonight you must be at the gate of the town. I shall make my way out with my attendant. Before the time fixed by you for surrendering the town to our enemies, the Lord will make use of me to rescue Israel. You must not ask what I intend to do; I shall not tell you until I have done it.' (Judith 8:32–34)

Judith fasted and prayed, asking God to give her a strong hand to carry out her plan. Then Judith removed the sackcloth she had been wearing, took off her widows' garments, bathed and anointed herself with fragrant ointment. She combed and dressed her hair and put on her most festive robe. She put sandals on her feet; she wore anklets and bracelets, rings and ear-rings and all her other jewellery. **Judith called her maid, gave her a skin of wine, a flask of oil, a bag filled with roasted grain, dried fruit – dates and figs and raisins – and fine bread, and a basket in which to carry them.**

The elders waiting for her at the gate were astounded at her appearance, amazed at her beauty, and they opened the gate for her and sent her off with their blessing. They watched her until she had gone down the mountain and had passed through the valley, until she and her maid were lost to their sight.'

The two women were intercepted by an Assyrian patrol and arrested. Judith told the men that she was fleeing from her people since they were going to be devoured, that she was on her way to see Holofernes to give him a true report, to show him how to capture all the hill country without losing a man.

The men were beguiled by Judith's beauty and by her good sense in escaping from the Israelites, and they escorted her to Holofernes' tent, where she found him resting on his bed under a canopy woven with purple and gold, with emeralds and other precious stones. He too was struck by Judith's beauty and he listened carefully while she told him lies about her people, how God was angry with them for breaking his laws and that for this reason they were going to be defeated. She told him of her plan to deliver the Israelites into his hands, and he was amazed at her wisdom.

Judith stayed in the camp for three days. Holofernes allowed her to eat her own food and to go to the spring to bathe and to pray. By the fourth day he could wait no longer to put his seduction plan into operation. To Holofernes'delight Judith, dressed in all her finery, lay down at his feet. Holofernes said, 'Drink with us and be merry!' and Judith replied, 'I will gladly drink, my lord, because today is the greatest day in my life.' Then she took what her maid had prepared and ate and drank with him. Holofernes drank a lot of wine, much more than he had ever drunk in any one day in his life.

Judith was left alone in the tent, with Holofernes stretched out, dead drunk. She prayed: 'Lord God, to whom all strength belongs, prosper what my hands are now to do for the greater glory of Jerusalem; now is the time to recover your heritage and to further my plans to crush the enemies arrayed against us.'

Holofernes' sword was hanging on the bedpost near his head. Judith took it down, took hold of his hair, struck his neck twice with all her might and cut off his head. She rolled his body off the bed and pulled down the canopy from the posts. Soon afterwards she went out and gave Holofernes' head to her maid, who placed it in the empty food basket.

It was late and all the servants had gone to bed. Unchallenged, the two women passed through the camp, circled around the valley and went up the mountain until they came to the city gates. From a distance Judith called to the sentries to open the gates, which they did in amazement that the women had returned.

Then Judith pulled the head out of the basket and showed it to them. She said: 'Glory to the Lord who has protected me in the course I took! My face seduced him, only to his own undoing; he committed no sin with me to shame me or disgrace me.'

As soon as it was dawn they hung Holofernes' head on the wall. Then they all took their weapons and went out to the mountain passes. When the Assyrians saw them they told their commanders, who went to Holofernes' tent to inform him, but there was no answer to their knocking. When the headless body was found the leaders of the Assyrian army tore their tunics and ran round the camp screaming. The men were overcome with fear. They fled across the plain and through the hill country, right into the hands of the Israelites.

Judith's great hymn of praise and thanksgiving can be found in the last chapter of her book. She returned home and stayed on her estate and for the rest of her life she was honoured throughout the whole country. She had many offers of marriage, but accepted none of them. No one ever again spread terror among the Israelites during Judith's lifetime, or for a long time after her death.

6 | Poetry and Wisdom Literature

Solomon chose wisdom. When God appeared to the young king in a dream and offered him anything he desired, Solomon chose a discerning heart so that he could rule God's people wisely. And God, always profligate with his gifts, was so delighted that Solomon had not asked for a long life, or wealth, or destruction of his enemies, that he gave him those things as well. (I Kings 13)

In the Old Testament, Wisdom is a desirable woman to be pursued and courted. She is an agent of the Most High God, calling us to fulfil our potential by following her counsels and by pointing out the pitfalls which would trap us in our folly. Wisdom's words are always beautiful and beguiling, and although the five 'Wisdom' books of the Bible themselves span a thousand years and the last (The Book of Wisdom) was written about 50BC, they are as relevant to us today as they were then.

For poetry and song in the Old Testament we have the collection of Psalms, and The Song of Songs. And, of course, there is poetry and song in many other books of the Bible considered under other specific headings.

Wisdom Literature

The Book of Job tells of a man who clings to God in blind faith and trust in the midst of terrible misfortunes, while Job's 'comforters' wrongly attribute his troubles to some sin.

Knowing there is a happy ending, I can almost enjoy Job sitting with his shard of pottery, scratching his sores, while his wife gets thoroughly fed up with him and urges him to 'Curse God and die.' And I quite like Job's reply: "You are talking like a foolish woman. Shall we accept good from God, and not trouble."

Since suffering was traditionally considered to be God's punishment for sin, this lovely book breaks new ground and completely overturns that thinking. 'Job' was revolutionary in its time.

Proverbs is a collection of wise sayings attributed to Solomon himself for, it seems, the benefit of a young man so that he may make his way securely in a secular, cynical and competitive society.

Proverbs begins with its own title and expressed purpose: *'The proverbs of Solomon son of David, king of Israel: for attaining wisdom and discipline; for understanding words of insight; for acquiring a disciplined and prudent life, doing what is right and just and fair.'*

The Book of Proverbs lends itself to quotation which can find resonance with men of any age. (*'A quarrelsome wife is like a constant dripping on a rainy day; restraining her is like restraining the wind or grasping oil with the hand.'* Pr 27:15-16) and the *Epilogue: The Wife of Noble Character* (Pr 31:10-31) has been known to produce many a smile from a congregation when read aloud in church – particularly when we reach the bit about not eating the bread of idleness!

Ecclesiastes: The author of this book is unknown (Qoheleth, son of David, king in Jerusalem, is merely a courtesy title), but whoever he was, he was not a happy man. His book begins with 'Meaningless! Meaningless!" says the Teacher. "Utterly meaningless! Everything is meaningless." (In the KJAV it was 'Vanity! . . .'). Even Wisdom is Meaningless; Pleasures are Meaningless; Toil is Meaningless. But there are glimpses of hope, and *'there is a time for everything, and a season for every activity under heaven* (Ch 3:1-8). And talking of God: *'He has made everything beautiful in its time. He has also set eternity in the hearts of men.'*

Ecclesiastes writes well of Wisdom and believes in God, so I think there is hope for him.

The Book of Wisdom comes from the Apocrypha (q.v. in the section 'Apocrypha').

Ecclesiasticus (Sirach) also comes from the Apocrypha and can be found in that section.

Psalms

The Psalms are poems, but they are also songs, and as such they were meant to be sung. Even now we 'recite' them in metrical chant, for not only were they the old Hebrew Psalter, they are also ours. The psalms are prayers, too, and they follow our prayer formulas now: Adoration; Contrition; Thanksgiving; Supplication. In both the Catholic 'Divine Office' and the Anglican 'Book of Common Prayer' and in other Christian liturgies, all 150 psalms are read or sung in the course of each month. We 'read the Office' at different times of day, no matter where we happen to be, no matter how we are feeling, because we know when we are praying the Psalms that we are joined with the whole Church. More than that, we are praying for people in the same situations as those expressed by the psalmist – for the hungry, the oppressed, the imprisoned, the sad, the joyful; those who suffer but hope, those who have reason to be thankful; those who are just hanging on to faith by their fingertips; those who are burdened with guilt, those in the pain of sickness or grief, those who don't know how to pray for themselves and those who have no-one to pray for them. It is all there in the psalms, the whole of humanity reaching out to God.

Some psalms have the name of the author (73 bear the name King David, who was an excellent musician and poet); others have titles which relate to the musicians, or their instruments, or the psalm settings, but many of the 'instructions' have lost their meanings since they were written.

'Psalms' is a collection of five books: 1-41; 42-72; 73-89; 90-106 and 107-150. After each psalm we say the doxology (*Glory be to the Father, and to the Son, and to the Holy Spirit. As it was in the beginning, is now, and ever shall be, world without end, Amen.*), and at the end of each 'book' in Psalms there is a similar form of praise to God. For example, at the end of Psalm 41 we find: '*Praise to the Lord, the God of Israel, from everlasting to everlasting. Amen and Amen.*' At the end of Psalm 72: *Praise to his glorious name for ever; may the whole earth be filled with his glory. Amen and Amen.* And so on . . .

The Song of Songs

The Song of Songs begins with a kiss and progresses from there. It is a wonderfully erotic love story, attributed to Solomon (which is why it is included in Wisdom literature), and it is not just any old love song,

126

but *The Song of Songs*. A Jewish Rabbi (Akiba) once said that, 'All the world is not worth the day that the Song of Songs was given to Israel. All the writings (*Ketubim*) are holy, but the Song of Songs is the holy of holies . . .' He is reputed to have been enraged when it was used as a drinking song.

Books have been written about the Song of Songs. The Cistercian, Bernard of Clairvaux (1090-1153), wrote 86 sermons on the Song of Songs for his monks – and in thirteen years, up to the time of his death, had failed to get past the beginning of the second chapter. He, like many another, saw in the Lover and the Beloved, the Bride and the Bridegroom, symbols of the human soul aflame for God.

The Song is often sexually suggestive, but never explicit. The woman (the Beloved) sometimes yearns and sometimes teases. We shall explore 'The Song' further with the herbs, Saffron, Turmeric, Henna and Walnut . . .

Poplar (II) ~ (*Populus euphratica*)

Plant description

Zohary says, 'The Euphrates Poplar is particularly characteristic of the bank (or flood) forest of the Jordan. Tolerant of a high degree of salt in the soil, this species of poplar, along with the wild date palm, grows in many of the springs of brackish water in the desert.' He then goes on to mention the dispute in the Talmud (the body of Jewish civil and ceremonial law and legend comprising the Mishnah and the Gemara) over the exact translations of *tzaftzafah* and *aravah* (which, I am happy to say, we need not concern ourselves with here). However, in early translations of Psalm 137 it was the *willows* on which the unhappy Israelites hung their harps, whereas in modern, perhaps more accurate versions, the trees were *poplars*. Zohary thinks the confusion may have arisen because the Euphrates Poplar displays two kinds of leaves: 'those of the younger shoots and branches, being oblong, are similar to those of the willow, while the leaves of the older shoots are ovate to rhombic and resemble those of the poplar.'

Be all that as it may, we have this wonderful, poignant lament of the Israelites in captivity in Babylon – which was built close to the Euphrates River (one of the four rivers which flowed out of Eden in Genesis). Here we have the Babylonians taunting the exiles by asking them to sing one of Zion's songs. Zion (Jerusalem), the holy city, God's dwelling place, once a great fortress, has been reduced to rubble by the invaders. No wonder the exiles are unable to sing in this alien land. A song telling of Zion's greatness, its beauty, its great God, would stick in their throats and choke them.

The psalmist vows never to forget Jerusalem. He would rather not play the harp again ('may my right hand forget its skill.'), never sing again ('May my tongue cling to the roof of my mouth').

Some parts of the psalm are quite savage with maledictions. This may have been partly hyperbole and partly because it was what the Israelites themselves suffered at the hands of the Babylonians when they were overtaken. This is poetry of great passion and wild imagery, like so many of the psalms, and we are fortunate that it has come down to us in the Jewish Psalter.

PSALM 137

By the rivers of Babylon we sat and
    wept
  when we remembered Zion.
There on the poplars
  we hung our harps,
for there our captors asked us for songs,
our tormentors demanded songs
    of joy;
they said, "Sing us one of the
    Songs of Zion!"

How can we sing the songs of the
    Lord
  while in a foreign land?
If I forget you, O Jerusalem,
  may my right hand forget its
    skill.
May my tongue cling to the roof of
    my mouth
  if I do not remember you,
if I do not consider Jerusalem
  my highest joy.

Remember, O Lord, what the
    Edomites did
  on the day Jerusalem fell.
"Tear it down," they cried,
  "tear it down to its foundations!"

O Daughter of Babylon, doomed to
    destruction,
  happy is he who repays you
  for what you have done to us –
he who seizes your infants
  and dashes them against the
    rocks.

Henna ~ (*Lawsonia inermis*)

Plant description

Henna is a member of the Willow-herb family. Zohary says, 'The henna 'tree' is a tree-like shrub up to 4m tall, branching heavily above, with ovate, opposite, entire leaves. It is impressive in spring when its bunches of small whitish fragrant flowers appear. Its fruits are many-seeded, small globular capsules torn at maturity. Although it is still found in Jericho and other villages in the Jordan Valley, and on the Coastal Plain, it has altogether disappeared from En Gedi.'

Zohary further says that its natural distribution area extends from tropical northeast Africa to Arabia, Persia and northwest India, and that although it was cultivated in very early times, its place of origin is unknown.

Plant lore

Zohary again: 'Henna is mentioned only in the Song of Solomon, which abounds in proverbial but not always realistic phrases. It is believed that henna, then as now, grew as an individual tree or in groups in courtyards for domestic use, but was not, as the Song of Solomon implies, a garden tree.

'It was grown mainly for its dye, which is prepared by crushing the dried leaves into a powder and mixing it with water to make a paste for application to various parts of the body, notably the nails and hair. Henna also dyes clothes permanently and is an ingredient of perfume, and its dense fragrant whitish flowers were offered in bouquets in Indian temples.'

The only reference to Henna in the Bible is found in the Song of Songs Ch 1:14 **'My lover is to me a cluster of henna blossoms from the vineyards of En Gedi.'**

Uses in modern herbal medicine

The leaves of this woody shrub have an astringent action. It grows in Egypt, in Iran and in India, where it has, in the past, been used to treat many conditions, including smallpox and leprosy. However, its most popular claim is as a dye for nails of hands and feet and, in Europe, for the hair.

Saffron ~ (*Crocus sativus*)

Plant description

The autumn-flowering saffron crocus belongs to the Iridaceae family of plants which grow from bulbs, corms and rhizomes.

The crocus is a tiny plant whose corm lies just under the surface of the soil and produces a tuft of narrow, grass-like leaves and relatively large blue flowers, each having six petal segments. It is the stamens and many thread-like golden stigmas which provide the precious dye. The colour 'saffron' needs no other description. It takes some two hundred crocuses to produce just one gram, which makes it such a valuable and desirable commodity.

There are cheap substitutes – like the safflower (*Carthamus tinctorius*), a thistle-like member of the family Compositae – but they lack the golden glow of the real thing.

Plant lore

In the myths of ancient Greece and Rome, Hymen, the god of marriage, wore saffron robes because that herb was said to have exhilarating effects. However, he didn't do too well with Orpheus and Eurydice: Orpheus won the heart of the beautiful nymph with his lute playing, and Hymen joined their hands, but his torch smoked instead of giving a clear golden flame – a bad omen realized later in tragedy.

Saffron is mentioned only once in the Bible – in the Song of Songs, when the Bridegroom is speaking of his delight in his Beloved. '. . . **nard and saffron, calamus and cinnamon, with every kind of incense tree, with myrrh and aloes and all the finest spices.**' (Ch 4:14)

Uses in modern herbal medicine

The flower pistils of the Saffron Crocus, gathered in autumn, are prepared as a powder or as a tincture, which both taste and smell aromatic. The actions of this herb are carminative, diaphoretic and emmenagogue – being used with benefit in amenorrhoea, dysmenorrhoea and in chronic uterine discharges.

Saffron is toxic if taken in large doses and should never be used in pregnancy.

Since this herb is so valuable and expensive, it is frequently adulterated (mixed with Safflower) or imitated by other yellow ingredients. There is a test for authenticity: pure Saffron should not produce a deposit when put in water, and it should not crackle when burnt.

Turmeric ~ (*Curcuma longa*)

Plant description

Zohary says, 'Turmeric is a tall herbaceous plant, native to southern Asia and the East Indies, and cultivated in China, Bengal and Java for its rhizomes. These are filled with a yellow or orange substance, which when crushed into a powder called curcumin is used to colour and flavour curries and to dye cloth. It contains an odorous, acrid, volatile oil used in pharmacy. It is sold in Arab markets as kurkum and is used both as a condiment and a medicinal drug.'

Because the rhizome is so important, Turmeric's flowers are rarely mentioned, and they themselves seem to feel their unimportance – hiding small, yellow, pineapple-shaped flower heads beneath long, elliptical leaves in the summer.

Plant lore

Once again we have arguments about translation. Zohary: 'Saffron (in Hebrew *karkom*) is mentioned only once in the Bible, in association with spikenard and cinnamon, spices imported from the Far East. Some commentators have identified it with *Curcuma longa*, the Indian turmeric of the Ginger family, others with true saffron, *Crocus sativas*, which was imported from neighbouring countries. The first species was never grown in this country (the Holy Land), and the second probably only in post-biblical times . . .

'Since the Arabic name for turmeric is *kurkum* and for saffron *saferam* and *kurkam*, there is linguistic support for both renditions. *Karkom* thus appears to be a homonym for two different plants in different periods.

'All Talmudic sources concerning *karkom* indicate a plant whose flowers were collected both for colouring and for healing purposes. In view of this and the fact that the garden saffron can easily be cultivated in Israel, while *Curcuma* cannot, there is no doubt that the sown *karkom* fields mentioned in the Mishnah refer to *Crocus sativus*.

Be all that as it may. We shall consider Saffron and Turmeric separately with regard to their modern uses, but put them together later in our journey through the Song of Songs.

Uses in modern herbal medicine

Turmeric has always been used widely in the East, particularly in Asia, where it is a key ingredient in curries and rice dishes, pickles and chutneys. More recently it has come under close scrutiny in the West for its medicinal properties. Not only has it proved to be antibacterial, but it has been found to prevent liver damage by alcohol and drug abuse.

Acetaminophen (Paracetamol) is a useful analgesic and diaphoretic when taken according to pharmaceutical directions, but in an overdose – even quite a small overdose – it can be lethal. The 'victim' seems well for a couple of days (there is no irritation of the stomach lining with this drug as there is with aspirin), but liver failure develops between the third and fifth days and is then irreversible. If Turmeric can be administered as an antidote at the crucial time, much damage and even death may be prevented.

There is more: Turmeric reduces cholesterol levels and has been found '*in vitro*' to have antiprotozoal properties – which augurs well for the battle against those single-cell, microscopic parasites bringing such diseases as Amoebiasis, Malaria and Sleeping Sickness.

Research on that other scourge, Alzheimer's Disease, has suggested that Turmeric has an important role to play in the protection of 'at-risk' cells in the brain.

This erstwhile merely culinary 'poor cousin' may well turn out to be an extremely valuable family member.

Walnut ~ (*Juglans regia*)

Plant description

The Walnut Tree is so attractive that it is often grown as a single specimen tree in gardens and parks. It rarely exceeds 20m in height, but has a pleasing symmetry with spreading branches and a reassuringly stout trunk which is deeply fissured and grey. Its leaves are not unlike those of the Ash, but larger and strongly scented. Male flowers hang in catkins, but female flowers appear in small, insignificant 'groups' at the tips of shoots; from these a large green 'fruit' develops. When ripe, but while still on the tree, the husk breaks open, shedding the nut. The delicious inner kernel is very rich in fat.

Zohary: 'The walnut is native to southeastern Europe, the Caucasus, northern Turkey, Persia and other West Asian countries, where it often forms steppe forests. It was already cultivated in biblical times and, along with other trees such as the white poplar, the pomegranate, the pistachio and the mulberry, was probably introduced into Canaan from Persia or Turkey . . .'

Plant lore

Zohary: (The early first-century historian Josephus) 'praised the fruitful valley of Genesareth for its abundance of walnut trees . . . and post-biblical literature often adverts to the walnut as a tree important in legend and ritual. A wealth of sayings and proverbs attests to its use not only for nuts but for oil, tannin and timber, and for wood for the altar fire in the Temple. Single walnut trees are still grown in all parts of Israel and there is even a place called the Valley of Walnuts in eastern Jerusalem.'

In The Song of Songs (Ch 6 v ll) the Lover says: *"I went down to the grove of nut trees to look at the new growth in the valley, to see if the vines had budded or the pomegranates were in bloom . . ."*

And, of course, walnut wood, with its lovely, distinctive grain is desirable for high-quality furniture.

Uses in modern herbal medicine

Walnut bark, leaves and fruits (nuts) are used in herbal medicine.

The Walnut itself is a good source of manganese and it is full of other nutrients which prevent atheroma (accretions, including cholesterol, which form as plaques in artery walls, causing blockage). We have been exhorted by researchers to eat nine walnuts each day to avoid the risk of heart disease. Walnuts, like most other nuts, are rich in vitamin E, masses of protein and lots of other goodies – all of which are powerfully antioxidant.

Dried walnut leaves are astringent and are useful in the treatment of skin diseases, such as herpes and eczema, while the powdered bark is a laxative.

THE SONG OF SONGS

'Let him kiss me with the kisses of
     his mouth –
for your love is more delightful
     than wine.
Pleasing is the fragrance of your
     perfumes;
Your name is like perfume poured
     out.'

So begins Solomon's 'Song of Songs' – not just any love song, but the most passionate, the most erotic, the most evocative, the most sensual, the most almost everything! In these eight chapters of lyric poems, undoubtedly sexually suggestive but never overtly explicit, superlatives abound in the lovers' descriptions of each other. They yearn for each other. They are intoxicated with love. The Beloved teases her Lover when he is present and becomes so desperate when he leaves her that she risks going out into the city alone at night to find him. Joy in each other's presence turns to desolation in absence. The words used are voluptuous, the imagery extravagant, and there is never any sense of shame in their displays of sexuality; on the contrary, there is often a reckless abandon. Towards the end, the Beloved's brothers are worried and debate about preserving their sister's honour, but she insists that her honour is not lost. (Perhaps this is the truth, but it sounds a pretty close-run thing and as her protectors they have every reason to be concerned.) If this were opera, one would be expecting a tragic climax, but here the lovers move towards the ecstasy of consummation, while we are simply left guessing about the final denouement.

The setting for this pastoral idyll is the countryside in springtime:

'My lover spoke and said to me,
     "Arise, my darling,
my beautiful one, and come with me.
     See! The winter is past;
          the rains are over and gone.

> Flowers appear on the earth;
>> The season of singing has come,
> the cooing of doves
>> is heard in our land.
> The fig-tree forms its early fruit;
> the blossoming vines spread their fragrance.
> Arise, come, my darling;
> My beautiful one, come with me."

The most exquisite and precious flowers and scents are employed to describe their beauty and desirability to each other:

> 'While the king was at his table,
>> my perfume spread its fragrance.
> My lover is to me a sachet of myrrh
>> Resting between my breasts.
> My lover is to me a cluster of henna blossoms
>> from the vineyards of En Gedi . . .'

The Lover feeds his Beloved: He has taken her off to the banquet hall, has strengthened her with raisins, refreshed her with apples, for she is faint with love. For him her lips drop sweetness like honeycomb, her garments are fragrant, she is spring enclosed, a sealed fountain. he tells her: **"Your plants are an orchard of pomegranates with choice fruits, with henna and nard, nard and saffron, calamus and cinnamon, with every kind of incense tree, with myrrh and aloes and all the finest spices. You are a garden fountain, a well of flowing water streaming down from Lebanon."**

And the Beloved replies:

> 'Awake, north wind,
>> and come, south wind!
> Blow on my garden,
>> that its fragrance may spread
>> abroad.
> Let my lover come into his garden
>> and taste its choice fruits.

The Song of Songs really needs to be read straight from the Bible, but I should like to finish with one of my favourite verses. In chapter 8, the woman, the Beloved, speaks:

> **'Place me like a seal over your,**
>> **heart,**
>
> **like a seal on your arm;**
> **for love is as strong as death,**
> **its jealousy unyielding as the grave.**
> **It burns like blazing fire,**
>> **like a mighty flame.**
>
> **Many waters cannot quench love;**
>> **Rivers cannot wash it away.**
>
> **If one were to give**
>> **all the wealth of his house for love,**
>> **it would be utterly scorned."**

So, whether one takes it at face value, as portraying passionate human love, or whether one looks on it as sacred because it portrays a soul (the Beloved) longing for union with God (the Lover), The Song of Songs, attributed to Solomon, is one of the most, if not *the* most beautiful love song ever written. For those who think that a soul's love for God could never burn with the intensity of human love, they should read the prayers of St Teresa of Avila (an editor preparing her prayers for publication once said he felt like an eaves-dropper listening in on a conversation between two lovers), of the poetry of St John of the Cross, or the writings of St Francis of Assisi and Clare of Assisi or of Thérèse of Lisieux.

Perhaps Rabbi Akibi's apparently sweeping statement was not so far wrong after all. And Bernard of Clairvaux must have been ecstatic with love for God when he wrote all those sermons on the Song of Songs[1]. Irenaeus, saint and martyr cAD200, considered that 'the glory of God is in the human person fully alive, and the life of humanity consists in the vision of God.'[2] I personally would be prepared to go along with that, because we are always more fully alive when in a relationship of passionate love, human or divine.

[1] See the section notes on 'Poetry and Wisdom Literature'.
[2] From the treatise '*Against the Heresies*' by Irenaeus.

7 | The Prophets

In all the centuries when God spoke through his prophets (from *c*800 to 400BC), not once did he advertise the job. There would have been no point; he wouldn't have had any eager applicants, with the possible exception of **Elisha**, who rather fancied himself wearing **Elijah's** mantle (and who filled the post rather well, as it happened). Most of them looked blank, or panic stricken, and most of them gasped the biblical equivalent of, 'Who, *me?*' Jonah just took to his heels and ran in the opposite direction, but God caught him in the end.

The prophets were God's agents, and almost all carried unpalatable truths which had to be delivered either to wayward nations, to corrupt leaders or to tyrannical kings. The practice of shooting a messenger of bad news reached its peak in those years and many of them came to a sticky end. One or two spoke of hope and of good times to come, but mostly on a 'carrot and stick' basis, and in prophets like **Micah**, who was sent to read the Riot Act to the unjust, the unmerciful and the proud, it has even been suggested that the more cheerful prophesy of restoration, triumph over Zion's enemies and reconciliation with God was tacked on at the end by someone else to soften the terrible threats in the book.

Amid all the thunder in Micah's book, in chapter six, we suddenly get a glimpse of a tender, loving, grieving God who wants to know why his people have turned away from him after all he has done for them: "My people, what have I done to you, how have I made you tired of me? Answer me!" And then Micah sets out, beautifully in simplicity and brevity, what God wants: 'And what does the Lord require of you? To act justly and to love mercy and to walk humbly with your God.'

Three different authors are said to have written the great visionary book of **Isaiah** (although the whole thing has always been on one scroll and for some a common author is assumed). It is just one of the many things we must leave scholars to argue about.

Some of the 'minor' prophets are included in the Bible simply because they happened to be written on the same scrolls as bigger names, but there are nuggets of pure gold hidden in their writings.

Amos, a simple shepherd from the southern kingdom was sent to prophesy in the north against the corruptions of wealth and extravagance, perversion of justice and the worship of false gods. His immediate reaction to God's call was to remind him that he (Amos) was a shepherd and a dresser of sycamore trees. And God probably said, "Yes, I know, but I've got a job for you and I would like you to start now."

Hosea had a rough ride too. He had to endure the pain and grief of an adulterous wife as an example of God's unconditional love for an unfaithful Israel, and God gave him his children's names to add to his burden: the first child, a daughter, was Lo Ruhamah, which means 'not loved'; his son was called Jezreel – a place of great bloodshed – and another daughter was Lo Ammi, which means 'not my people'. But for all his misery and misfortune, Hosea's book contains one of the loveliest prophesies, when God speaks to Israel: "Therefore I am now going to allure her; I will lead her into the desert and speak tenderly to her." There is a happy ending to Hosea because God effects a reconciliation between Hosea and Gomer, his prostitute wife. I hope he changed the children's names too.

I don't know exactly how one could describe **Daniel**. He is not a prophet in the accepted meaning of the word, although the placing of his book of adventures seems entirely appropriate. Daniel, probably of noble birth, was carried off into exile in Babylon, together with some of his friends (notably Shadrach, Meshach and Abed-Nego who had a brush with Nebuchadnezzar's fiery furnace but survived). Daniel acquired great prestige and honour as a seer from his gift of explaining the king's dreams, and although he was once thrown into a lions' den (the poor lions nearly starved to death because they refused to eat him) he lived to a good age and appears to have died from natural causes.

Jeremiah has never enjoyed a good press, which is a pity because he starts out as a nice young Jew who just wants to get on with his life like everyone else. We shall make his closer acquaintance and tell his story with the herb, 'Wormwood' And we shall meet **Ezekiel** later, too, when we consider the herb, 'Nettle'. **Jonah's** story will feature a Castor Oil Plant.

The books of the prophets can be divided into three main sections: First, those who prophesied the fall of Jerusalem to Babylon in 587BC (**Isaiah, Joel and Micah**). Second, those who prophesied at the time of Jerusalem's fall and during the exile in Babylon (**Jeremiah, Habakkuk and Zephaniah**). Third, those who prophesied at the time of the return from Babylon, beginning in 538BC (**Haggai, Zechariah and Malachi**).

Others had special assignments: **Hosea and Amos** were sent to prophesy to Israel, the northern kingdom, which fell to Assyria in 722BC. **Jonah and Nahum** were prophets to Nineveh, the Assyrian capital. **Daniel** was a young aristocrat in exile in Babylon, but lived quite comfortably at court most of the time. **Ezekiel** spoke words of hope to Jewish exiles in Babylon, and **Obadiah's** call was to Edom – Israel's old enemy.

Mostly these men were sent on 'missions impossible'. God sent them to his wilful, wayward people as last-ditch attempts to turn the hearts of his people, Israel, back to him. It never worked. Israel seems to have had a self-destruct button and never listened to the prophets until it was too late; then these same prophets were called upon to preach hope and forgiveness and reconciliation to a grieving and contrite nation. However, there was one notable success: the prophet Isaiah spoke in the time of the good King Hezekiah and Jerusalem was saved from the powerful Assyrian king (Sennacherib) because his advice was taken.

And so, the Israelites were locked into a cyclical pattern of sin, punishment, repentance, reconciliation and forgiveness. Poor long-suffering God.

Castor Bean ~ (Ricinus communis)

Plant description

The Castor Bean is related to the family, Euphorbiceae, which includes the spurges. It is native to India and to Israel, where it is found growing quite happily in neglected places, even in desert wadis, which are dry except in the rainy season. Its seeds have been found in ancient Egyptian tombs, some 6,000 years old, but its place of origin is unknown.

This is a fast-growing, shrubby tree with large palmate leaves which afford good shade. Male and female flowers, carried close together on the same plant, give way to capsular fruits, each separate cell of which carries a single large seed. The seeds are striped dark and light brown and they are highly poisonous. The seed's endosperm is rich in oil as well as the deadly toxin, ricin, which causes liver damage, severe gastro-enteritis and heart failure.

The Castor Bean tree is said to be susceptible to infestation by a specific worm which can kill it very quickly.

Plant lore

Zohary gives just one reference in the Bible for this plant. **'And the Lord God appointed a *plant*, and made it come up over Jonah, that it might be a shade over his head, to save him from his discomfort. So Jonah was exceedingly glad because of the plant. But when dawn came up the next day, God appointed a worm which attacked the plant, so that it withered'** (Jonah 4:6-7 KJAV)

Nowhere is the castor bean actually mentioned by name, but Zohary says that the Hebrew *kikayon* appears in the Bible only in this passage and that it is rendered differently in various translations. However, 'None of these fits the context better than the castor bean . . . All the other plants suggested (e.g. 'vine') are creeping or straggling.'

Uses in modern herbal medicine

Although the expressed oil of the Castor Bean seed is cathartic and purgative, its action is mild and therefore suitable even for young children and pregnant women. Castor Oil is useful for removing worms after other remedies have been administered.

Externally, Castor Oil can be used for the treatment of ringworm and other itchy skin conditions.

Some people find Castor Oil nauseous, but its taste can be covered by other, more pleasant oils, or it may be given in fresh or warmed milk.

JONAH AND THE CASTOR OIL PLANT
(Better known as Jonah and the Whale)

The book of Jonah takes up very little space. It occupies just two or three pages, a mere four chapters, in the Old Testament, in the section reserved for the prophets. It has been described as a light satire, with no pretensions to being historical, but it teaches the depths of God's love and forgiveness to everyone.

The Ninevites, who at that time were as bad if not worse than the people of Sodom and Gomorrah, come out of it rather well in the end, since they repent of their wickedness, but poor old Jonah . . .

One day God spoke to Jonah, son of Amittai. "Go to the great city of Nineveh," he said, "And preach against it, because it is a wicked place."

Jonah took to his heels and ran, not towards Nineveh, but away from God. At Joppa, he boarded a ship bound for Tarshish and sighed with relief at having escaped. No way was he going anywhere near Nineveh!

Perhaps God was amused, perhaps he was angry, we are not told. Anyway, there was a great storm at sea and the ship was in danger of breaking up. The terrified sailors cried out to their own gods and tried to lighten the ship by throwing cargo overboard, but this made not the slightest difference.

Jonah, no doubt exhausted by all that running, had gone below deck and was sleeping when the captain shook him awake: "How can you sleep? Get up and call on your god; perhaps he will save us from perishing," he said.

In the meantime, the sailors had decided to cast lots to find out who was responsible for their plight, and the lot fell on Jonah, who had to admit that his God, the God of heaven who made the sea and the land, was after him for disobedience.

Jonah said he was sorry; it was all his fault; but if they threw him overboard the sea would become calm again. To give the sailors their due, they tried to row ashore, but the sea became even wilder, so they prayed to Jonah's God as they threw Jonah into the sea that they wouldn't be punished. To their amazement the sea became calm, 'So the sailors offered a sacrifice to the Lord and made vows to him.'

And the Lord provided a great fish to swallow Jonah, and Jonah was inside the fish for three days and three nights before it vomited him on to dry land.

Jonah was in a much more amenable mood when God spoke to him a second time: "Go to the great city of Nineveh and proclaim the message I gave you," he said.

This time Jonah obeyed. He went to Nineveh and told them that in forty-nine days the city would be destroyed and all the people with it.

Jonah couldn't believe what happened next: The Ninevites turned to God. They declared a fast, and every one of them put on sackcloth and sat down in the dust. The king made a great proclamation about fasting and penance: everyone was to call urgently on God; they were to give up their evil ways and their violence. "Who knows," said the king. "God may yet relent and with compassion turn from his fierce anger so that we will not perish."

And indeed, when God saw that they had turned away from wickedness he had compassion on them and didn't carry out his threat of destruction.

But instead of being pleased with what had happened, Jonah was angry with God. He (Jonah) had told the people of Nineveh that they were due to perish in forty-nine days, and now it wasn't going to happen. He sat and sulked.

God spoke gently to Jonah, much as a loving parent might speak to a petulant child. "Have you any right to be angry, Jonah?"

Jonah didn't answer God. He went out, built himself a makeshift shelter and waited to see what would happen to Nineveh. But Jonah hadn't made a very good job of building a shelter and he was hot and uncomfortable, so God provided a plant to grow up quickly to give extra shade.

In spite of his bad temper, Jonah was pleased with the plant, but at dawn the next morning God provided a worm, which chewed the plant so that it withered. Later, God sent a scorching wind which, combined with the sun blazing on Jonah's head, made him feel ill and faint. Jonah wanted to die, but God said to him, "Jonah, do you have any right to be angry about the plant?"

Jonah said, "Yes, I do. I am angry enough to die."

Then God said to Jonah, "You are concerned about the plant that gave you shade, although you didn't plant it or tend it. It just sprang up overnight. But Nineveh has more than a hundred and twenty thousand people who cannot tell their right hand from their left, and many cattle as well. Should I not be concerned about that great city?"

Jonah's reply is not recorded.

Nettle ~ (*Urtica dioica*)

Plant description

The Common Nettle (Stinging Nettle, a member of the Urticaceae family) is an erect annual herb which grows up to 1m in height. It has heart-shaped, pointed, toothed leaves which grow in opposite pairs direct from the main stem. These leaves are densely covered with tiny hairs which release histamine and other irritant substances when touched, producing a burning rash. Unisex flowers grow in creamy-green clusters which hang from the leaf axils, and fruits are minute nutlets enclosed in green sepals. Nettles grow mostly on waste ground and in woods. They are despised in gardens, but butterflies love them and they can be a great attraction for the Peacock, Red Admiral and Comma in summer months.

Plant lore

'To grasp the nettle' is to confront a difficult situation and to cope with it boldly (on the grounds that a nettle is less likely to sting if taken and held firmly). Aaron Hill, mid-18th century poet and playwright advocated this line of defence/attack:

> Tender-hearted stroke a nettle,
> And it stings you for your pains;
> Grasp it like a man of mettle,
> And it soft as silk remains.

And in his play, Henry IV, Shakespeare plucks the flower 'safety' from the nettle 'danger'.

The nettle has many biblical references although, again, there is argument over translation and it can be found as 'brier' or 'weed' when the context begs 'nettle'.

Freshly picked, young nettles can be boiled and eaten as a green vegetable which resembles spinach in both taste and appearance. (Nettles lose their capacity to sting when cooked or dried.) A word of caution: old nettles, particularly uncooked old nettles, can cause kidney damage.

Nettle leaves can be used for making a green dye, and nettle has been known as 'poor man's flax' since nettle fibre can be used for making coarse cloth.

Nettle is useful in skin preparations because of its astringent properties and in lotions and shampoos to stimulate circulation to hair follicles in the scalp.

Perhaps we shouldn't treat it with such contempt when it appears in our gardens, but harness its better qualities and let it be for the benefit of butterflies.

Uses in modern herbal medicine

As Chevallier says, the Nettle is too well known to need any introduction and it hardly needs cultivation. Young shoots are picked as a spring tonic and are used as a vegetable; older leaves and stems are picked in summer, when the plant is in flower, for medicinal use. The root is harvested in autumn.

The Nettle's key actions are diuretic, tonic, astringent and anti-haemorrhagic; the leaf increases lactation and the root reduces prostatic enlargement.

Nettles are rich in vitamins and minerals. The leaves are nutritious, containing appreciable quantities of minerals and iron, which can be of value in treating anaemia.

Nettle leaves are known to stimulate the removal of uric acid by the kidneys, therefore making it useful in the treatment of gout and other arthritic conditions. It is markedly diuretic, probably due to flavonoids and its high potassium content.

The constituent, glucoquinone, reduces blood sugar levels, providing additional treatment in non-insulin dependent diabetes. The Nettle is also strongly haemostatic.

Nettle preparations are: Infusion (leaf); capsule, tincture and juice.

First and foremost, the Nettle is a detoxifying herb – increasing urine output and the elimination of waste products, especially urates. For this reason, it is valuable in the treatment of gout and osteo-arthritis, especially where poor kidney function and fluid retention are a feature. The Nettle is also known to aid connective tissue repair and regeneration.

As an effective haemostatic, Nettle will slow or stop bleeding and so is helpful in menorrhagia. A high iron content makes Nettle a key herb for chronic blood loss and the anaemia which accompanies it.

The Nettle also has an anti-allergenic activity, and it may be taken for hay fever and asthma as well as for nettle rash (urticaria). It is found in many prescriptions for skin conditions such as acne, eczema and psoriasis, and it is thought to improve lactation. The root is now a specific for enlarged prostate and is often combined with Saw Palmetto for this purpose.

Topically, this herb can be applied to itchy skin conditions, and the juice is used to treat Nettle stings!

Dioscorides lists many uses for Nettle, including the chopped leaves as a plaster for septic wounds and dog bites, and the juice for nose bleeds.

The Nettle combines well with other herbs: with Saw Palmetto for enlarged prostate; with Elderflower for hay fever; with Celery and Devil's Claw for gout, and with Burdock, Dandelion and Echinacea for acne and other skin conditions.

PROPHET OF HOPE

As prophets go, Ezekiel is a rare bird. He is an optimist. His message might be much the same as the other prophets – repentance for sin and a returning to God – but it is couched in different terms. Perhaps that is because Ezekiel is in exile in Babylon and life there isn't too bad. Those carried off into exile were the ones useful to Babylon and, generally speaking, they held good positions in the land, whereas those left behind in Judah, particularly in the devastated capital city of Jerusalem, were a rabble more or less left to fend for themselves.

Ezekiel's call comes in a vision right at the beginning of his book. He says, ". . . While I was among the exiles by the Kebar River, the heavens were opened and I saw visions of God . . . "

Ezekiel is shown a windstorm coming out of the north – an immense cloud with flashing lightning, surrounded by brilliant light. The centre of the fire looked like glowing metal, and in the fire were four living creatures, in the shape of men, but with four faces and four wings each, and they moved at great speed on wheels. He describes these creatures in great detail. Then, says Ezekiel, he saw the glory of God. Above the creatures' heads there was a sapphire throne and a figure like that of a man. From the waist up he looked like glowing metal, as if full of fire, and from the waist down he was fire, and brilliant light surrounded him. 'Like the appearance of a rainbow in the clouds on a rainy day, so was the radiance around him.' Between the winged creatures and God's glory was an expanse, sparkling like ice and awesome. Ezekiel can only fall face down and, trembling, wait.

God's first instruction is for Ezekiel to stand up, then he is told what he has to say to the Israelites, that rebellious house who may well not be inclined to listen to Ezekiel and who certainly won't welcome his message. God makes his usual promise to his new prophet: **"And you, son of man, do not be afraid of them or their words. Do not be afraid, though briers (nettles) and thorns are all around you and you live among scorpions."**

Then Ezekiel sees an outstretched hand, offering him a scroll to eat, which has the words of prophesy written on it. Ezekiel writes: "So I ate it, and it tasted as sweet as honey in my mouth." His mission is local – he is to speak to the Israelites in exile with him in Babylon, those who have absorbed the customs of their 'adopted' land, and who now worship the false god Baal.

There are so many visions and fantastic allegories, and so much 'Godly play' that Ezekiel's book needs to be read straight from the Bible. Chapter 37 is the best known of all:

'The hand of the Lord was upon me, and he brought me out by the Spirit of the Lord and set me in the middle of a valley; it was full of bones. He led me to and fro among them, and I saw a great many bones on the floor of the valley, bones that were very dry. He asked me, "Son of man, can these bones live?"

'I said, "O Sovereign Lord, you alone know."

'Then he said to me, "Prophesy to these bones and say to them, 'Dry bones, hear the word of the Lord! This is what the Sovereign Lord says to these bones: I will make breath enter you, and you will come to life. I will attach tendons to you and make flesh come upon you and cover you with skin; I will put breath in you, and you will come to life. Then you will know that I am the Lord.'"

'So I prophesied as I was commanded. And as I was prophesying, there was a noise, a rattling sound, and the bones came together, bone to bone. I looked, and tendons and flesh appeared on them, but there was no breath in them.

'Then he said to me, "Prophesy to the breath; prophesy, son of man, and say to it 'This is what the Sovereign Lord says: Come from the four winds, O breath, and breath into these slain, that they may live.' So I prophesied as he commanded me, and breath entered them; they came to life and stood up on their feet – a vast army.

'Then he said to me: "Son of man, these bones are the whole house of Israel. They say, 'Our bones are dried up and our hope is gone; we are cut off.' Therefore prophesy and say to them: 'This is what the Sovereign Lord says: O my people, I am going to open your graves and bring you up from them. I will put my Spirit in you and you will live, and I will settle you in your own land. Then you will know that I the Lord have spoken, and I have done it, declares the Lord.'"

And so, Ezekiel prophesies Israel as one nation under one king and the Lord's desire that Israel will once again be his people, and he will be their God. The Temple of the Lord will be rebuilt in Jerusalem and it will again be holy – a fitting place for God's presence.

A rare bird indeed, this prophet of hope.

Wormwood ~ (*Artemisia herba-alba. A absinthium*)

Plant description

The White Wormwood, a member of the Compositae family, is a small shrub no more than 50cm in height and densely branched from its base. Leaves are grey, hairy, deeply cut and aromatic; they yield a juice which is extremely bitter. Stems and branches bear small yellow flowers in late summer that are arranged in heads comprising several florets. Tiny fruits have tufts of hair to aid to dispersal by wind.

Plant lore

'Wormwood' applies to any woody shrub of the genus *Artemisia* which includes *A. absinthium*, from which absinthe and vermouth are made. (The green liqueur, absinthe, was the downfall of many in literary and artistic circles in the late 19th and early 20th century, and Emile Zola (1840-1902) wrote of the misery it caused and of the horrific effects of absinthe poisoning. Its manufacture and sale are now illegal.

A pretty lethal combination of absinthe and brandy probably contributed to Oscar Wilde's death: he loved the colour of the liqueur and said a glass of absinthe was as poetical as anything in the world – and it suited his style!

In C.S. Lewis' wonderful book, 'The Screwtape Letters', the young trainee devil, Wormwood, under the guidance of his much more experienced uncle, Screwtape, is assigned to bring about the damnation of a young man who has just converted to Christianity. This book comes highly recommended!

But our herb, the white wormwood, grows in desert places and is eaten by goats freely enough (keeping them free from intestinal worms). According to Zohary, the dried leaves are used to prepare a tea drunk by the Bedouin of the Sinai and the Negev, which presumably has the same beneficial effect on them as on the goats.

In the Bible, wormwood is often paired with gall and always refers to bitterness, to poison, to something unpalatable, causing sickness.

In Proverbs, Solomon gives advice to his son about women (prostitutes): **'For the lips of a strange woman drop as an honey-**

comb, and her mouth is smoother than oil: But her end is as bitter as wormwood, sharp as a two-edged sword. Her feet go down to death; her steps take hold on hell.' (Proverbs 5:1-8 KJAV)

Wormwood was often used by God in his messages to the Israelites through his prophets (particularly Amos and Jeremiah).

Uses in modern herbal medicine

Wormwood is an aromatic bitter which improves bile flow, stimulates the appetite and helps in the digestion of fatty food. It is also anti-parasitic, anti-inflammatory and mildly anti-depressant when depression is associated with sluggish liver function. Wormwood is quite commonly included in prescriptions for cancer treatment when patients suffer from loss of appetite and debility. As its name suggests, Wormwood is also used to expel intestinal worms.

Wormwood must be used in very small doses and only for short periods. It should not be taken in pregnancy, or when there is peptic ulceration or gastritis. It is contra-indicated in hypertension, where there is known heart disease and in epilepsy.

A FIRE SHUT UP IN THE BONES

Jeremiah was a nice young Jew from a priestly family, quiet and unassuming by all accounts, who simply wanted to get on with his life like everyone else, trying to ignore the great Babylonian threat to Judah. But when God gets an idea into his head, and makes his choice of person to carry out his work, he can't be shifted. Jeremiah certainly tried to persuade God that he wasn't the right man for the job, but better men than Jeremiah had foundered on that particular rock before, and he might as well have saved his breath.

Unappreciated as it might have been, God's call to Jeremiah is lovely; he says, "Before I formed you in the womb I knew you. Before you were born I set you apart; I appointed you as a prophet to the nations."

Jeremiah's response is not one of pleasure or gratitude. "Ah, Sovereign Lord," I said, I do not know how to speak; I am only a child." God has heard that sort of excuse many times before and is not impressed by it; he simply reaches out his hand, touches Jeremiah's mouth and says, "Now I have put my words in your mouth. See, today I appoint you over the nations and kingdoms to uproot and tear down, to destroy and to overthrow, to build and to plant."

God doesn't let Jeremiah get a word in – he shows him, first, a branch of an almond tree, just to make sure his new prophet is paying proper attention, then he shows him a boiling pot, tilting away from the north and tells Jeremiah to get started. God says, " Get yourself ready! Stand up and say to them whatever I command you. Do not be terrified by them, or I will terrify you before them. Today I have made you a fortified city, an iron pillar and a bronze wall to stand against the whole land – against the kings of Judah, its officials, its priests and the people of the land. They will fight against you but will not overcome you, for I am with you and will rescue you."

Same pattern as usual: commission followed by promise.

And so, Jeremiah is sent off. In the course of his ministry his scrolls are destroyed (by the king), he has to be rescued from a muddy cistern where he has been lowered to rot to death, and he is thrown into prison because he refuses to stop prophesying.

In Jeremiah 20, there is a heart-rending complaint to God . . . Oh Lord, you deceived me, and I was deceived; you overpowered me and prevailed. I am ridiculed all day long; everyone mocks me. Whenever I speak, I cry out proclaiming violence and destruction. So the word of the Lord has brought me insult and reproach all day long. **But if I say, "I will not mention him or speak any more in his name, his word is in my heart like a fire, a fire shut up in my bones. I am weary of holding it in; indeed, I cannot . . ." '**

And in chapter 23:15, God tells Jeremiah to prophesy against the prophets themselves who have been worshipping false gods and leading the people astray: "Therefore, thus says the Lord of hosts concerning the prophets: **'Behold, I will feed them with wormwood, and give them poisoned water to drink.' "** (KJAV)

There are 52 chapters in the book of Jeremiah, and these are followed by his 'Lamentations' when what he has been prophesying for some forty years finally comes to pass and Jerusalem is destroyed by Nebuchadnezzar's army in 587BC. This was terrible. Jerusalem was God's city; his Temple was there, but now everything has been razed to the ground and the people have been carried off into captivity in Babylon.

The laments are outpourings of grief. They are graphic depictions of defeat, forced labour, rape and cruelty, of a people starving to death; they are dirges of a people now crying out to the God they had ignored and whose prophets they had killed.

But even in this deep sorrow there is hope of restoration to God's favour. In the Fifth (and last) Lamentation the people ask God to look on their degradation and to save them: 'Make us come back to you, Yahweh, and we will come back. Restore us as we were before!'

God does eventually restore them, of course, but the Israelites are not released from exile until 539BC when men like Ezra and Nehemiah have key roles in re-building Jerusalem and God's Temple.

Wormwood and poisoned water to drink indeed.

THE
NEW
TESTAMENT

8 | The Gospels

The word 'Gospel' is derived from the old English 'godspel', which means 'good news'. What good news? The coming of God's rule – the coming of the Kingdom of God. For me, the Kingdom of God is summed up by the mystic, Caryll Houselander:

> Christ looked at the people.
> He saw them assailed by fear:
> He saw the locked door;
> He saw the knife in the hand;
> He saw the buried coin;
> He saw the unworn coat,
>   consumed by moth;
> He saw the stagnant water
>   drawn and kept in the pitcher,
>   the musty bread in the bin –
>   the defended,
>   the unshared,
>   the ungiven.
> He told them then
>   of the love
>   that casts out fear;
>   of the love that is four walls
>   and a roof over the head:
>   of the knife in the sheath,
>   of the coin in the open hand,
>   of the coin given
>   warm with the giver's life,
>   of the water poured in the cup,
>   of the table spread –

the undefended,
the shared,
the given –
the Kingdom of Heaven.

The Gospels give four different accounts of the life of Jesus of Nazareth. There is a great overlap of material, but with each writer we are shown different aspects of the One they each knew as the long-awaited Christ. As far as time of writing is concerned, all we know with any certainty is that all four were written in the latter half of the first century. Which came first? Good question, and that is something else we must leave to scholarly argument. Traditionally, it was Mark, who would have received his information from Peter (although Mark probably knew Jesus, and if he were the unidentified youth in the Garden of Gethsemane on the eve of the crucifixion, as seems likely, Jesus was probably his hero).

Between them, the Gospel writers tell us all we know of the life on earth of Jesus, the Christ. From them we learn the manner of his conception and nativity, but there is tantalisingly little about his childhood and early adulthood. All we know of those hidden years is that he was obedient to his parents after getting 'lost' for three days in Jerusalem at the age of about twelve and that he probably worked for his father, who was a carpenter. Jesus of Nazareth makes no further appearance in Scripture until his baptism by John in the River Jordan at the age of thirty, receiving the gift of the Holy Spirit and God's commission before embarking upon a gruelling three-year ministry of preaching and healing. This ministry was mainly in Galilee, but Jesus did visit Jerusalem, where head-on clashes with the authorities finally led to his arrest there one Passover, where, after a very cursory trial, he died an agonizing and ignominious death on a reclaimed rubbish-tip called 'Golgotha' – the Place of the Skull- outside the city wall. Hardly an appropriate profile for the Messiah the Old Testament prophets had promised would come to deliver Israel from bondage.

To find out 'what happened then' it is necessary to read the Gospels for oneself. Reading *about* them is totally inadequate. Apart from the Gospels, there is little first-hand information about Jesus' life. Josephus, the most reliable historian writing at the time did refer to Jesus of

Nazareth, a miracle-worker who was put to death by Pontius Pilate; and Tacitus (Roman senator and historian *c*AD56-120) made a fleeting reference to Jesus in his explanation of who the Christians were when reporting about those being put to death by Nero. Discovery of the Dead Sea Scrolls (writings of a Jewish sect living at the same time of Jesus) has thrown no further light on Jesus, although they have greatly added to our knowledge of ancient Palestine and its philosophies.

In studying the Gospels, it is necessary to look closely at the authors – four very different personalities; four entirely different styles; one message conveyed in four different ways. But always One Lord.

Matthew is a Jew, writing in Hebrew for Jews. Matthew wants to demonstrate that the Old Testament (Covenant) is fulfilled in Jesus and that therefore he must be the Messiah. Sixteen times he says 'This was to fulfil what the Lord had said through the prophet.' Matthew's Jewishness is also seen in his attitude to the Law: Jesus did not come to destroy the Law but to fulfil it.

Matthew begins his Gospel with a genealogy which goes from Abraham to King David; from King David to the exile to Babylon; after the exile to Joseph, the husband of Mary, of whom was born Jesus, who is called Christ. In all, forty-two generations. Matthew, the ex-tax collector, makes a wonderful job of tracing Jesus' descent from the first great patriarch. Matthew gives us the birth narrative, quoting Isaiah's prophesy: "The virgin will be with child and will give birth to a son, and they will call him Immanuel" which means, "God with us". Matthew gives us the visit of the Magi, bearing gifts to the Child – gifts fit for a king. Matthew gives us the Lord's Prayer; his own calling from his tax booth; miracles of healing; wonderful parables; the great Sermon on the Mount; the Woes of the Pharisees (of which, more later); the Crucifixion, the Resurrection and, finally, the Great Commission when the eleven remaining disciples are sent out to make disciples of all the nations with the great promise: . . . "And surely I am with you always, to the very end of the age."

Mark writes in Greek, but not very good Greek. Mark 'speaks' quickly, like an excited child; his imagery is vivid and memorable. In the original

Greek he is in such a hurry that he gets his tenses mixed up, but by the time it gets to our New Testament the translators have sorted out his grammar and his Gospel has been 'tidied up'. Mark writes down what Peter tells him happened, so that we hear Peter himself speak. Mark is simple and dramatic. His Gospel goes at great speed, full of little details so that we can have no doubt that these things actually happened. Three things in Mark's Gospel stand out for me:

He says that the crowd sat down on the green grass (Ch 6:39) – which places the feeding of the five thousand in spring because in summer the grass scorches to brown and doesn't recover until spring.

In his telling of the awful night of Jesus' arrest in the Garden of Gethsemane a youth loses his white linen shirt when he is grabbed by a soldier and runs away naked. Surely it must have been the young John Mark himself for no-one else mentions it, and the 'upper room' where Passover was celebrated in Jerusalem – the scene of the Last Supper – was probably in his parents' house (Ch 14:51-52).

Mark (who is involved with Paul in Acts of the Apostles and who is mentioned quite frequently in Paul's letters to the churches) gives the names of two sons of Simon of Cyrene – Rufus and Alexander (Ch 15:21). He can't possibly have known them at the time. Simeon Niger – the dark one, which Simon would have been since he came from North Africa – appears again in Acts 13 with others from Cyrene. Something monumental must have happened to Simon as he carried Our Lord's cross to Calvary for him to have become a Christian.

Mark is desperate for us to see Jesus the man, and God in that man. He wants us to know Jesus.

Luke's Greek is elegant. He is 'the beloved physician', an educated man, a gentile – the only non-Jewish New Testament writer. And Luke writes for gentiles, in particular for someone called 'Theophilus'. Luke's outstanding characteristic is the universality of his Gospel: Jesus is for all men and women, saints and sinners alike, without distinction. Luke begins his Gospel with the annunciation to Zechariah whose wife, Elizabeth will give birth to John the Baptist, and the Annunciation to Mary. Through Luke we have Mary's visit to her cousin Elizabeth, Mary's Magnificat, and Zechariah's song – our Benedictus.

Luke ends his Gospel with the Ascension, but continues his narrative in his second treatise to Theophilus in the book we know as 'Acts'.

John's Gospel is also in Greek, and it is quite different from the others – very beautiful, philosophical and theological. One must always look for a deeper meaning underlying John's words. John's material is different too: he omits most things that the other 'synoptic' gospels have written about and adds a lot of new material, as if he were filling in gaps. In John's Gospel we meet Jesus cooking breakfast on the shore of Galilee for the disciples after he has risen from the dead, and John finishes with that lovely verse: 'Jesus did many other things as well. If every one of them were written down, I suppose that even the whole world would not have room for the books that would be written.'

From John we have the picture of Christ as King and God. For John, the Cross is Christ's throne.

EPIPHANY
(The Manifestation of Christ to the Magi: The Feast Celebrated on 6th January)

We have given them exotic names:
Caspar, Melchior, Balthazar.
We have interpreted their gifts:
Gold for kingship,
Frankincense for divine priesthood,
Myrrh for suffering and death.

We too must follow the star,
bring our gifts.
They knelt in the straw to look
into Mary's eyes,
bowed low
to see the Christchild in the manger –
And so must we.

(P.A.)

Gold is not a herb, of course, but a high-density metallic element which occurs naturally in quartz and gravel and which cannot be destroyed by chemical reaction. It is the stuff of legend. Men have died for it and have killed to acquire it. Empires have fallen because of it.
Gold denotes kingship.

Frankincense is a costly fragrant resin from the shrub *Boswellia sacra*, imported in biblical times by The Phoenicians via the spice route across southern Arabia. (See 'Frankincense' back in the Old Testament 'Pentateuch' Section on God's Holy Recipes.)
Frankincense denotes priesthood.

Myrrh can be found back in the same Old Testament section with Frankincense, Cassia and Cinnamon. It too is an aromatic resin (obtained from the small bush, *Commiphora abyssinica*). Myrrh was used to embalm the bodies of the dead.
Myrrh is the gift for one who is to die.

Between them, the Gospels of Matthew and Luke tell the story of Jesus' birth. Matthew writes: 'This is how the birth of Jesus Christ came about: His mother Mary was pledged to be married to Joseph, but before they came together, she was found to be with child through the Holy Spirit. Because Joseph her husband was a righteous man and did not want to expose her to public disgrace, he had in mind to divorce her quietly.

'But after he had considered this, an angel of the Lord appeared to him in a dream and said, "Joseph, son of David, do not be afraid to take Mary home as your wife, because what is conceived in her is from the Holy Spirit. She will give birth to a son, and you are to give him the name, Jesus, because he will save people from their sins." ' (Matthew 1:18-21)

Jesus is the Greek form of Joshua, which means 'The Lord saves'.

We have to go to Luke's Gospel for more details of the birth narrative, and Luke is at pains to say how thorough and careful his investigations have been before writing to Theophilus.

Luke begins with Elizabeth and Zechariah. Then follows the Annunciation to Mary (our 'Angelus' and the inspiration for much great art). Luke tells of Mary's visit to her cousin Elizabeth ('The Visitation') and Mary's song of thanks to God (the 'Magnificat'). With the birth of John – who will be the Baptist – we have Zechariah's outpouring of praise and prophesy (the 'Benedictus').

In Luke we find the whole Christmas scene: the census and the journey to Bethlehem; shepherds and angels; Mary and Joseph with the Christchild lying in a manger in a stable, and the Presentation of Jesus in the Temple on the 8th day, when old Simeon speaks his lovely 'Nunc Dimittis', most familiar to us in sacred music in the words of the King James Authorized Version of the Bible:

'Lord, now lettest thou thy servant depart in peace, according to thy word:
For mine eyes have seen thy salvation,
Which thou hast prepared before the face of all people;
A light to lighten the Gentiles, and the glory of thy people Israel.'

Luke ends his account 'When Mary and Joseph had done everything required by the Law of the Lord, they returned to Galilee to their own town of Nazareth. And the child grew and became strong; he was filled with wisdom, and the grace of God was upon him.'

But now we must return to Matthew (Chapter 2) for the visit of the Magi. Traditionally there were three of them, said to be wise men, possibly kings. They were obviously skilled in the natural sciences; philosophers, perhaps; astrologers certainly, prepared to make a very long journey to follow a star of such brightness that it must surely have foretold the birth of a king.

In Matthew alone, it says: 'After Jesus was born in Bethlehem in Judea, during the time of King Herod, Magi from the east came to Jerusalem and asked, "Where is the one who has been born king of the Jews? We saw his star in the east and have come to worship him."

'When King Herod heard this he was disturbed, and all Jerusalem with him. When he had called together all the people's chief priests and teachers of the Law, he asked them where the Christ was to be born. "In Bethlehem in Judea," they replied, "For this is what the prophet has written:

"But you, Bethlehem, in the land of Judah,
are by no means least among the rulers of Judah;
for out of you will come a ruler who will be the shepherd of my
people, Israel."

(Micah 5:2)

'Then Herod called the Magi secretly and found out from them the exact time the star had appeared. He sent them to Bethlehem and said, "Go and make a careful search for the child. As soon as you find him, report to me, so that I too may go and worship him."

'After they had heard the king, they went on their way, and the star they had seen in the east went ahead of them until it stopped over the place where the child was. When they saw the star they were overjoyed. On coming to the house, they saw the child with his mother, Mary, and they bowed down and worshipped him. **Then they opened their treasures and presented him with gifts of gold and of incense and of myrrh.** And having been warned in a dream not to go back to Herod, they returned to their country by another route.'

From William Barclay we have various suggestions about the star. Certainly around the time of Jesus' birth there were some unusual phenomena. He says: 'About 11BC, Halley's comet was visible, shooting brilliantly across the skies. About 7BC there was a brilliant conjunction of Saturn and Jupiter. In the years 5-2BC there was an unusual astronomical phenomenon: In those years, on the first day of the Egyptian month, Mesori, Sirius, the dog star, rose heliacally, that is at sunrise, and shone with extraordinary brilliance. Now, the name *Mesori* means *the birth of a prince*, and to those ancient astrologers such a star would undoubtedly have meant the birth of some great king. We cannot tell what star the Magi saw; but it was their profession to watch the heavens, and some heavenly brilliance spoke to them of the entry of a king into the world.'

Also from Barclay (also in his commentary on the Gospel of Matthew, volume 1), we get a good insight into the character of Herod the Great, who was half Jew and half Idumaean with Edomite blood in his veins. 'He had made himself useful to the Romans in the wars and civil wars of Palestine, and they trusted him . . . He was the only ruler of Palestine who had ever succeeded in keeping the peace and in bringing order into disorder. He was a great builder; indeed, he built the Temple in Jerusalem. He could be generous. In times of difficulty he remitted taxes to make things easier for people; and in the famine of 25BC he had actually melted down his own gold plate to buy corn for the starving people.

'But Herod had one terrible flaw in his character. He was almost insanely suspicious . . . If he suspected anyone as a rival to his power, that person was promptly eliminated. He murdered his wife Mariamne and her mother, Alexandra. His eldest son, Antipater, and two other sons, Alexander and Arostobulus, were all assassinated by him. Augustus, the Roman Emperor had said, bitterly, that it was safer to be Herod's pig than Herod's son . . .'

Back to Matthew's Gospel: 'When Herod realised that he had been out-witted by the Magi, he was furious, and he gave orders to kill all the boys in Bethlehem and its vicinity who were two years old and under . . . Then what was said through the prophet Jeremiah was fulfilled:

"A voice is heard in Ramah, weeping and great mourning,
Rachel weeping for her children and refusing to be comforted,
Because they are no more." '

(Jeremiah 31:15)

The Massacre of the Innocents (whose Feast Day is the 28th December) echoes another massacre some two thousand years earlier at the time of Moses' birth. On this later occasion, Joseph was warned in a dream to flee, and so the Holy Family became refugees in Egypt until Herod died and they were able to return, not to Bethlehem but to a small town called Nazareth in Galilee.

Carob ~ (*Ceratonia siliqua*) (The Locust Bean)

Plant description

Zohary describes the Carob Tree as: 'a medium-sized evergreen, its trunk often gnarled and densely branched on top to form a globular to somewhat oval crown. The leaves are divided into two to four pairs of ovate, entire leaves. The flowers are unisexual, males and females growing on different trees and crowded in short spikes on old thick branches. They are small and greenish and appear in autumn, but the fruit does not mature until late in the following summer. It is a dry, fleshy, indehiscent*, many-seeded brown pod, shed when ripe. The sweet pulp, from which a kind of syrup is prepared by the Arabs, may contain as much as fifty per cent sugar and is edible by man and livestock.' Zohary adds: 'Significant in many plant communities, the carob tree is common in the Coastal Plain and the adjacent foothills, and on the eastern slopes of Galilee and Samaria.'

Here, we must also mention the insect, since there is argument as to whether the 'locust' as food for John the Baptist in the New Testament was the locust bean or the insect: The locust is a member of the Acrididae family, a grasshopper well known in Africa and Asia, which flies in great migrating swarms, destroying all vegetation in its tracks.

Plant lore

Zohary gives more valuable information: 'The carob tree, annually producing quantities of sweet fruit, is native to Israel and is important in the local vegetation. It is astonishing that although it has undoubtedly been common in the Land since ancient times, it is not mentioned in the Old Testament and is only hinted at in the New Testament, although its Hebrew name *haruv* often appears in the Mishnah and the Talmud and is also preserved by the Arabs of southwestern Asia and North Africa . . .

'The story of John (which gave rise to the carob's other name – St John's Bread), recalls the story in the Talmud about the Jewish sage Rabbi Shimeon Bar-Yohai, who while hiding in the Galilean caves with his son for fear of capture by the Romans, was said to have been sustained for twelve years on carobs alone.'

*does not split open when ripe

Apparently – because of the colour of the bean and its high sugar content – the carob is used as a substitute for chocolate.

Uses in modern herbal medicine

The Carob bean is the edible, horn-shaped, fleshy seed-pod of the evergreen leguminous tree. The bean itself is highly nutritious and sustaining, but mostly the leaves are used in an infusion in herbal medicine to improve digestion and to reduce fevers. In the past it was used in South America, particularly in Brazil, for treating venereal disorders, and it was said to be successful in relieving syphilitic skin lesions.

Carob has a sedative effect on the nervous system and has been used in epilepsy. Its taste is refreshingly bitter, rather like tea.

A VOICE CRYING IN THE WILDERNESS

'In those days, John the Baptist came preaching in the Desert of Judea and saying, "Repent, for the kingdom of heaven is near. This is he who was spoken of through the prophet Isaiah:

> "A voice of one calling in the desert,
> 'Prepare the way for the Lord,
> make straight paths for him."

John's clothes were made of camel's hair, and he had a leather belt around his waist. **His food was locusts and wild honey.** People went out to him from Jerusalem and all Judea and the whole region of the Jordan. Confessing their sins, they were baptised by him in the River Jordan.' (Matthew 3:4-6)

For four hundred years there had been no prophet in Israel; no-one to speak God's word to the people. 'There was no voice, nor any that answered'. Then, from the Desert of Judea, there suddenly appeared a wild man preaching repentance for sin and the coming of the kingdom of heaven. (Matthew 3).

The Baptist's appearance is even more sudden in the Gospels of Mark (Chapter 1) and John (Chapter 1). He draws large crowds. He is thought to be a re-incarnation of the prophet Elijah (In 2 Kings 1:8 there is a description of Elijah: 'He was a man with a garment of hair and with a leather belt around his waist.'). Jewish priests come to question John.

They ask: "Who are you?" John says that he is not the Messiah, nor is he a prophet, he is merely, 'A voice of one calling in the desert, "Prepare the way for the Lord, make straight paths for him." (See Isaiah 40:3-5)

We have met John before, albeit in his pre-natal state, in what we celebrate as The Visitation (See Luke 1):

> Here are such wonders met:
> Young Virgin and aged kinswoman embrace,
> womb reaching out to womb.
>
> One babe leaps for joy,
> The other, not yet quickened, not yet fully formed,
> lies quiet
> in the depths of his mother's praiseful pondering.
>
> (P.A.)

Thirty silent years have passed since that encounter of the mothers. We know nothing of John in that time and, apart from an incident when Jesus was 'lost' for three days when the rest of the family were on their way home from Jerusalem when he was twelve years old, nothing of Jesus either, except that he went home to Nazareth and was obedient to his parents.

In iconography, St John the Baptist is the Forerunner, and that is all he ever claimed to be. Some Pharisees asked why, if he were not the Christ, or Elijah the prophet, he was baptising. "I baptise with water," John replied, "but among you stands one you do not know. He is the one who comes after me, the thongs of whose sandals I am not worthy to untie."

When Jesus came from Galilee to the Jordan to be baptised at the beginning of his ministry, John tried to deter him. He said, "I need to be baptised by you, and do you come to me?" But Jesus persuaded him that it was right that he himself should be baptised, 'to fulfil all righteousness.' John consented, and it was done.

As Jesus came out of the water the heavens opened and the Spirit of God descended, like a dove, and lighted on him. And a voice from heaven was heard to say, "This is my Son, whom I love; with him I am well pleased."

To say that John was unpopular in some quarters would be a massive understatement. He was fierce and uncompromising in his condemnation of Pharisees and Sadducees, to their faces and in very public places. And how the downtrodden Jews must have loved hearing those in authority being called 'vipers'.

Royalty didn't escape John's tongue either, which led to John's arrest, imprisonment and eventual murder: Herod Antipas was married, but seduced his brother Philip's wife, Herodias, and persuaded her to leave Philip and to marry him. In order to do this, he had to 'put away' his own wife. Leaving aside the moral aspect of the situation, Herod had broken two laws: he had divorced his own wife without cause, and he had married his sister-in-law, which was prohibited under Jewish law while the brother still lived.

Rebuking any tyrant carries an automatic health warning, and John had signed his own death warrant. Herod Antipas was bad enough, but his new wife, Herodias, was something else when it came to revenge. Then there was Salome, the daughter of Herodias by her first marriage.

Salome danced for Herod at his birthday party, and Herod was so delighted (and probably so drunk) that he promised with an oath to give her whatever she asked. Young Salome conferred with her mother, who said, "Ask for the head of John the Baptist on a platter."

It is said that Herod was distressed, but that because of his oath in the hearing of all his dinner guests he could not refuse Salome. Distressed or not, he ordered that her request be granted. John was beheaded in prison and his head was brought in on a platter and given to the girl, who carried it to her mother.

John's disciples came and took his body and buried it, then they went and told Jesus. When Jesus heard the news and the circumstances of John's death he went away, by boat, privately, to a solitary place and he grieved for John.

Anise ~ (*Pimpinella anisum*)

Plant description

The annual herb, Anise, is small and delicate with bright green leaves; its basal leaves are entire and toothed, while the upper leaves are feathery. Anise bears umbels of insignificant, pale green flowers followed in early autumn by tiny seeds.

Anise is quite picky about its growing conditions: it will not thrive in cold or damp, but give it a light dry soil and a sunny position and it will respond by producing good flowers and plenty of aromatic seed.

Plant lore

The anise seed (aniseed) has many culinary and medicinal uses. In England, it has been cultivated as a kitchen herb from medieval times, and probably longer since its beneficial properties were well known throughout Europe in those days. It was used in ancient Rome and Egypt too.

Liqueurs (the delicious *anis* of France), curries, cakes, sweets, cooked fruit and vegetables, all benefit from the distinctive flavour of the crushed seeds of anise, which yield their aromatic oil so freely.

We mention anise here because it is such a valuable addition to our domestic storehouse of flavours and medicaments. Disappointingly, although it has one Bible reference (Matt 23:23 in the KJAV), it is probably an error in translation. Zohary describes the plant, but then writes that it is more than doubtful whether anise has ever been grown in biblical countries. Ratcliffe agrees; he says that, according to the best authorities, anise, as given in the KJAV, should have been translated as 'dill'.

No matter, the sheer poetry of the KJAV has sustained many millions of people over the past few centuries and we can enjoy its beauty still. **'Woe unto you, scribes and Pharisees, hypocrites! for ye pay tithe of mint and anise and cummin, and have omitted the weightier matters of the law, judgement, mercy and faith . . .'**

Uses in modern herbal medicine

This member of the Carrot family originally came to us from Egypt and North Africa, but the ancient Greeks and Romans knew it as a spice and used it in remedies for chest complaints.

English herbalists have long used Anise as a carminative and digestive stimulant and to improve lactation in nursing mothers. Anise also has an antispasmodic action and will help to relieve dysmenorrhoea as well as distressing bronchospasm in asthma and whooping cough. It will also act as an expectorant.

Anise is rich in minerals and vitamins, and with its sweet, characteristic taste it is a popular ingredient of cough medicines and throat lozenges.

Cumin ~ (*Cuminon cyminum*)

Plant description

Zohary describes Cummin (which is how both he and Scripture spell this herb) as: 'an annual herb with an erect stem branching above; each branch terminates in a composed umbel of minute flowers. The leaves are deeply incised into long capillary lobes. The small elliptical and hairy fruits consist of two carpels which are the cummin grains, widely used for flavouring bread and dishes. It is also used in folk medicine as an antispasmodic and its oil is an ingredient of perfume.'

Ratcliffe adds the information that cumin belongs to the Parsley family of plants with deeply incised fennel-like leaves which, like the common hedge parsley, heads up with umbels of minute white or pink flowers followed by twin-carpel, aromatic, highly flavoured fruits.

Plant lore

As well as our reference with anise, dill, mint and rue in Matt 23:23, there is a lovely passage in Isaiah 28:23-29 when the prophet has been warning of destruction because of the behaviour of the people who have fallen away from God:

23. 'Listen and hear my voice; pay attention and hear what I say.
24. When a farmer ploughs for planting, does he plough continually? Does he keep on breaking up and harrowing the soil?
25. **When he has levelled the surface, does he not sow caraway and scatter cummin?**
    Does he not plant wheat in its place, barley in its plot, and spelt in its field?
26. His God instructs him and teaches him the right way.
27. **Caraway is not threshed with a sledge, nor is a cartwheel rolled over cummin; caraway is beaten out with a rod, and cummin with a stick.**
28. Grain must be ground to make bread; so one does not go on threshing it for ever.
    Though he drives the wheels of his threshing cart over it his horses do not grind it.
29. All this also comes from the Lord Almighty, wonderful in counsel and magnificent in wisdom.'

Uses in modern herbal medicine

Cumin is a digestive, widely used with other herbs in Ayurvedic medicine to improve liver function. Cumin's taste and smell slightly resemble those of anise, but are less pleasant; nevertheless, Cumin is used as both spice and carminative and it has value in veterinary medicine.

Dill ~ (*Anethum graveolens*)

Plant description

Dill, an annual herb of the Parsley family (Umbelliferae), is sufficiently pleasing to the eye to be grown in the garden, where it appreciates a sunny but sheltered spot in well-drained soil with faithful watering, particularly in dry spells. It is best kept away from other strongly aromatic herbs, like fennel, since cross-pollination 'contaminates' the dill and spoils its own more delicate flavour.

Young plants of Dill and Fennel are so similar in appearance that they can be confused. However, even at that stage, Dill smells more like caraway, while Fennel has the stronger smell, more like aniseed.

The main stem grows up to 0.75m high and its hollow sub-stems bear glaucous, finely-feathered leaves. From mid-to-late summer, umbels of yellow florets are carried aloft and these give way to the seeds in early autumn. Dill should be cut in bunches and hung upside down in paper bags so that the flat, oval, dark brown seeds can be collected when fully ripe. Dill is mostly cultivated to supply a growing demand, but in temperate climates it grows wild quite happily in fields.

Plant lore

We have already explored the confusion of translation in the Bible of dill with anise, and we shall be using the same reference in St Matthew's Gospel later.

Dill is a valuable herb in the kitchen; its leaves are used in salads and in dishes that require delicate flavouring that will not overwhelm. (It goes particularly well with fish.) Pickled cucumber is often flavoured with dill.

'Dill' can refer to a simpleton, someone who has fallen victim to a trickster, but strangely, 'Dilly' means a remarkable person or thing, as in 'an absolute dilly'.

Uses in modern herbal medicine

Dill is another herb from the mists of time, being first recorded some 3,500 years ago.

This herb is aromatic (resembling caraway in taste, and yet distinct from it), tonic, mildly diuretic and antibacterial. It has long been used to promote lactation in nursing mothers – and an added bonus from that is the carminative effect it has on their babies through their milk. In fact, Dill's main medicinal use is as gripe water for babies with colic and 'wind'. Dill seeds, chewed after a meal, sweeten the breath and aid digestion for adults too.

Mint ~ (*Mentha longifolia. Mentha spicata*)

Plant description

Mint belongs to the family Labiatae (which also includes rosemary) and family members can be identified by their square stems and by a corolla or calyx divided into two parts, suggesting lips – hence the name. 'Mint' is the name given to any aromatic plant of the genus *mentha*.

Mint is a perennial herb whose rhizomes (roots) are extremely vigorous and can be invasive if not contained. It can grow as tall as lm on its erect, hairy stems. Leaves are lanceolate, hairy and sharply toothed (not unlike the nettle, except they don't sting). Masses of tiny flowers are borne aloft in attractive purple spikes. Mint has both a distinctive smell and an easily recognizable taste

Although essentially a kitchen garden herb, Mint will grow quite happily almost anywhere so long as it is provided with moisture. Zohary says that in the Holy Land it grows freely along ditches and water courses and in swamps.

Mints are thought to have originated in Eastern Asia and are said to possess a very complex genetic pattern that allows prolific hybridisation. For this latter reason, certain identification of Mint in the Bible is difficult. Some botanists think that biblical Mint was Common Mint – also known as Horse Mint *Mentha longifolia*, but others argue that it could have been Spearmint: *Mentha spicata*. Peppermint – *Mentha piperita* may have been grown for medicinal purposes in biblical times, but it is impossible to be sure about this.

Plant lore

In Greek, Mint is *Minthe*, so called from a nymph of that name with whom Pluto (ruler of the infernal regions in mythology) was besotted. Pluto's wife, Proserpine, quite naturally thought little of this and turned her rival into a herb to be plucked and eaten.

Mint must be our most familiar herb, it is used in so many different ways. It can be pickled in vinegar for mint sauce and mint jelly, added to soups and many meat and fish dishes, added as flavouring to vegetables and served as a syrup with fruit salads. It can be used to decorate glasses of

Pimm's, as iced mint tea on a hot summer's day or served as delicious mint julep (a sweet, iced drink made with bourbon if you happen to live in America, whisky anywhere else). There are those who will not eat lamb without the accompaniment of mint in one form or another. Dried mint, both leaves and flowers, are used in pots pourri, laid in linen drawers for their fragrance and moth-repellent properties and added to other scented herbs in cushions.

Mint is involved in a 'scene' in the Bible when, with several other herbs, it becomes a source of contention and makes Jesus extremely angry (Matthew 23:23)

Uses in modern herbal medicine

Peppermint is used widely in medicine today, being prescribed for a variety of different conditions. Peppermint Oil relieves Irritable bowel syndrome (IBS) by reducing inflammation of the colonic mucous membrane. A Peppermint teabag prepared as an infusion with boiling water left to cool before drinking can provide swift relief for mild upsets of the stomach such as dyspepsia, flatulence and gastritis.

Since the volatile oil of Peppermint contains menthol (a consistent component of cough and cold remedies), it is effective in relieving blocked airways – nasal and bronchial passages and sinuses – by inhalation.

A compress of crushed mint leaves will help to relieve migraine; 'rheumatic' joints benefit from mint rubbed on to the painful parts; a few drops of Peppermint Oil in a footbath will pamper tired feet; oil in a cold spray is a blissful remedy for sufferers with hot flushes and it is also good for the hair!

Rue ~ (*Ruta graveolens*)

Plant description

Rue (the European *Ruta graveolens*), is a perennial evergreen shrub which grows to a height of 1.2m. Its glaucous, bi-pinnate leaves are heavily aromatic and bitter to the taste. Rue's yellow flowers are also heavily scented.

Zohary describes the very similar *Ruta chalepensis* as: 'a dwarf shrub native to Israel and other Mediterranean countries. The common rue grows in the 'bathah' (dwarf- shrubbery) formations where its yellow flowers and heavy scent render it very striking. It is a richly branching plant with abundant dissected leaves covered throughout with oil-bearing glands. Its flowers have a green calyx and 4-5 yellow fringed petals about lcm long. The fruit is a small capsule with dark seeds.'

Rue is grown as an ornamental plant, as a condiment, and for the essential oil distilled from its leaves.

Plant lore

In Shakespeare's 'Hamlet', Ophelia, in her madness of grief at Hamlet's rejection of her and at her father's death, distributes flowers: Rosemary for remembrance, pansies for thoughts, fennel and columbines and rue which, she says, may be called herb of grace o' Sundays. (Rue was known as 'The Herb of Grace' because it was used for sprinkling holy water.)

St Luke's account of 'The Woes of the Pharisees' in chapter 11 of his Gospel is very similar to that of St Matthew's in chapter 23 of his Gospel. However, Luke gives rue with mint, whereas Matthew gives mint, dill and cummin. This is the only time in the whole of Scripture that rue is referred to directly (under its Greek name, 'peganon' since Luke was writing in Greek).

Uses in modern herbal medicine

Rue is no longer much used in herbal medicine because other plants serve the same purpose with fewer attendant risks.

Traditionally, Rue was used as a protection against evil and was considered to be one of the most powerful antidotes to poisons, particularly to venomous snakebites, and against plagues. It was also widely used in diseases of the eye.

One of Rue's main 'attributes' was known to be stimulation of the uterine muscles, and therefore it was used as an abortifacient. Needless to say, it should never be used during pregnancy.

THE WOES OF THE PHARISEES

No wonder they hate him! This is no 'gentle Jesus, meek and mild.' This is a man in the full flood of righteous wrath, unleashing the most terrible denunciation, exposing the hidden faults of the Pharisees and, to their fury and humiliation, doing it in a very public place to the obvious delight of the ordinary people. Jesus is magnificent in his fury and his audience applauds his audacity. Only John the Baptist ever dared to speak out against the Pharisees like this, and it is wonderful to see these distinguished and pretentious men so discomfited. They think they have an innate superior sanctity, but in fact they spend their lives fault-finding and making life miserable for the working classes.

But Jesus never encourages anyone to beak the law; he never puts a foot wrong and it is difficult for the scribes and Pharisees, those most dedicated of legalists, to trap him in his words. And they are burning to trap him. Great crowds follow Jesus wherever he goes to hear him preach love and peace and hope. He understands their worries, their sickness, their weariness. He is their Teacher, a rabbi with a difference, and they love him.

The Pharisees follow Jesus around, watching and listening from a safe distance; they plant their paid sympathizers in the crowd wherever he goes. They fear him and therefore they hate him. They want rid of him and their impotence against him galls them to the depths of their being.

God's actual commandments to his people, a sound, simple social structure based on love of him and of everyone else, have been broken up into countless little rules and regulations so that it is hardly possible to blink without committing some transgression. For example, the Law says that a man must not work on the Sabbath day, but by the time the scribes finished with that it was laid down how many paces a man might walk on the Sabbath, how heavy a burden he might carry and all the things he might and might not do – some of them quite ludicrous. Now there are some fifty volumes in small print to contain all the minutiae associated with God's original Law, and half the time no one knows whether they are sinning or not.

Another example of ridiculous interpretation: The tithe forms an important part of Jewish Law. It is written quite clearly in many places in the Pentateuch: 'You shall tithe all the yield of your seed, which comes forth from the field year by year.' (Deuteronomy 14:22) And, 'All the tithe of the land, whether of the seed of the land or of the fruit trees is the Lord's; it is holy to the Lord.' (Leviticus 27:30) However, God's law on tithes has been added to by the lawyers, who maintain that anything edible, preserved or taking its nourishment from the soil is to be included. Of dill, they said the seeds, leaves and stalks must be tithed. Every man must lay aside one-tenth of his produce for God, no matter how small his crop. So, a man keeping a small patch in his vegetable garden for herbs, just for his family's use, is tithed in the same way as someone who has a vast field of produce for sale. Ridiculous? Yes, and Jesus thinks so too.

Jesus has been coming to a rolling boil for some time now. He has endured potentially incriminating questions set by the Pharisees' disciples, fielding each one neatly and making them look foolish. Some of the questions have been couched in flattery: "We know you are a man of integrity and that you teach the way of God in accordance with the truth. You are not swayed by men, because you pay no attention to who they are. Tell us then, what is your opinion? Is is right to pay taxes to Caesar or not?"

Their intention was transparent; Jesus was more than a match for them. "You hypocrites!" he said. "Show me the coin used for paying the tax." They brought him a denarius, and he asked them, "Whose portrait is this? And whose inscription?" "Caesar's," they replied. Then he said to them, "Give to Caesar what is Caesar's, and to God what is God's."

Some Sadducees – a Jewish sect who don't believe in the resurrection of the dead like the Pharisees – came to Jesus, all obsequious smarm, tongue-in-cheek, to ask him a convoluted question about marriage at the resurrection. They were sent away confounded too, and the crowds were astonished at his teaching.

Then, hearing that Jesus had silenced their own disciples and the Sadducees, the Pharisees got together. One of them, a particular expert in the Law, tested him with the question, "Teacher, which is the greatest commandment in the Law?" Jesus replied, "Love the Lord your God with all your heart and with all your soul and with all your mind. This is the first commandment. And the second is like it: Love your neighbour as yourself. All the Law and the Prophets hang on these two commandments.'

Then Jesus turned the tables and asked them a question they couldn't answer: "What do you think about the Christ? Whose son is he?"

The trap snapped shut when they answered, "The son of David" and Jesus pointed out that David had called the Messiah 'Lord', and how could he have done that if the Messiah was his son? No-one could say a word in reply, and from that day no-one dared to ask him any more questions.

But Jesus wasn't finished with *them*, not by a long chalk. He launched into a searing, scathing attack of the Pharisees:

"Woe to you, teachers of the law and Pharisees, you hypocrites! You shut the kingdom of heaven in men's faces. You yourself do not enter, nor will you let those enter who are trying to.

"Woe to you, teachers of the law and Pharisees, you hypocrites! You travel over land and sea to win a single convert, and when he becomes one you make him twice as much a son of hell as you are.

"Woe to you, blind guides. You say 'If anyone swears by the temple, it means nothing; but if anyone swears by the gold of the temple, he is bound by his oath. You blind fools! Which is greater: the gold, or the temple that makes the gold sacred? You also say, 'If anyone swears by the altar, it means nothing; but if anyone swears by his gift on it, he is bound by his oath.' You blind men! Which is greater: the gift on the altar, or the altar that makes the gift sacred? Therefore, he who swears by the altar swears by it and by everything on it. And he who swears by the temple swears by it and by the one who dwells in it. And he who swears by heaven swears by God's throne and by the one who sits on it.

"Woe to you, teachers of the law and Pharisees, you hypocrites! You give a tenth of your spices – mint, dill and cummin. But you have neglected the more important matters of the law – justice, mercy and faithfulness. You should have practised the latter, without neglecting the former. You blind guides! You strain out a gnat but swallow a camel.

"Woe to you, teachers of the law and Pharisees, you hypocrites! You clean the outside of the cup and dish, but inside they are full of greed and self-indulgence. Blind Pharisee! First clean the inside of the cup and dish, and then the outside also will be clean.

"Woe to you, teachers of the law and Pharisees, you hypocrites! You are like whitewashed tombs, which look beautiful on the outside but on the inside are full of dead men's bones and everything unclean. In the same way, on the outside you appear to people as righteous but on the inside you are full of hypocrisy and wickedness.

"Woe to you, teachers of the law and Pharisees, you hypocrites! You build tombs for the prophets and decorate the graves of the righteous. And you say, 'If we had lived in the days of our forefathers, we would not have taken part with them in shedding the blood of the prophets.' So you testify against yourselves that you are the descendants of those who murdered the prophets.' Fill up, then, the measure of the sin of your forefathers!

"You snakes! You brood of vipers! How will you escape being condemned to hell?" (Matt 23:13-33)

No wonder they hate him. They fear him and they are plotting to kill him.

Mustard ~ (*Sinapis arvensis*)

Plant description

The mustard plant is an annual herb which belongs to the Brassica (cabbage) family. Large leaves covered in stinging hairs – which can cause an irritating rash – are arranged at the base of the plant. A central stem, growing to a height of 1.5m, branches to small umbrels composed of myriad tiny yellow flowers. Slender pods each contain a dozen or more minute seeds.

Zohary says: 'The mustard of the New Testament is probably *Brassica nigra*, source of the important condiment, black mustard, which has long been extensively cultivated and was in biblical times the source of mustard-seed oil and a medicament. Evidence for its identity is that it is the tallest plant in the local species of *Sinapis* and *Brassica*, often 2m and more in height; and since it is conspicuous in the vegetation around the Sea of Galilee and farther north, it suits the context of the parable, as does the small size of its seeds (1mm) . . . Mustard is not mentioned in the Old Testament, but it is often referred to in the Mishnah.'

Plant lore

Mustard has many good culinary and medicinal uses: it can be eaten when a mere seedling to add piquancy to cress for 'mustard and cress', or its seeds can be crushed and mixed to a paste for use as a spicy condiment But mustard has also been employed for more sinister purposes: Mustard gas, a vapour with powerful irritant and vesicant properties has been made from the colourless oily liquid from the plant and used in warfare against infantry (particularly in the First World War, 1914-1918).

There are three references to the mustard seed in the New Testament – Matthew 13:31-32; Mark 4:30-32 and Luke 13:18-19, and they all refer to the same parable which Jesus used to teach the crowd by the lakeside. The three accounts are practically 'word-for-word' so that there is, in effect, just one mention of mustard seed in the whole Bible.

Uses in modern herbal medicine

Mustard seeds are irritant, stimulant, diuretic and emetic.

Mustard has long been used in a poultice to relieve distressing and painful chest conditions (such as pleurisy and bronchitis) and for painful 'rheumatic' joints. The volatile oil of Mustard is a powerful irritant which can be put to good use as a rubifacient to increase blood flow to a painful area, to heat it, to cause it to sweat and thus to expedite the disposal of toxins. A word of caution here: Mustard is a vesicant and can cause severe blistering if too much is used or if it in left on the skin too long.

Taken internally, Mustard seeds are laxative, but they can cause gastritis in all but the smallest amounts.

THE PARABLE OF THE MUSTARD SEED

When St Matthew was writing his Gospel, he must surely have spent a long time sitting with pen in hand, just remembering how it had been when Jesus lived on earth.

Matthew had a good memory for details, for keeping records and for putting them down accurately. Matthew, ex-tax collector, remembered only too well how his fellow Jews despised him for selling himself into the service of the occupying Romans. In our time we would have called Matthew a quisling, and there must have been some appropriate and equally uncomplimentary words to describe such a man then too. Matthew, with very few friends, feared and considered contemptible by his own people, was not a happy man.

Then, one day, Jesus walked past Matthew's booth and said, "Follow me." Just like that, just those two words, and to his own amazement and relief and joy, Matthew got up and followed him.

Later that day Matthew threw a party. Jesus was there, so were his disciples, and so, apparently, were some undesirable characters of much the same ilk as Matthew. This infuriated the Pharisees, who wanted to know why Jesus was eating with such people. Can't you hear them almost spitting out the words, 'tax-collectors and sinners'! Matthew remembered Jesus' reply, and he set it down, exactly as it was said all those years before: "It is not the healthy who need a doctor, but the sick. But go and learn what this means: 'I desire mercy, not sacrifice.' For I have not come to call the righteous, but sinners."

Jesus was quoting the prophet Hosea (Ch 6:6) to his critics who were supposed to be experts in Scripture and the Law. Not a good way to make friends in high places, but then Jesus did always identify best with the unloved and the marginalised.

Meticulous as ever, Matthew has set out 'A record of the genealogy of Jesus Christ, the son of David, the son of Abraham . . .' A whole page, full of names from the earliest times in the Old Testament to the birth of Jesus, the Christ.

The birth narrative is there; the visit of the Magi; the flight into Egypt; the massacre of the innocents; the return to Nazareth.

Now Matthew is getting closer to familiar ground. He writes of John the Baptist preparing the way and of Jesus being baptised in the River Jordan; of Jesus being driven into the desert to be tempted for forty days and forty nights. He records the calling of the first disciples and how Jesus went throughout Galilee, 'teaching in the synagogues, preaching the good news of the kingdom and healing every disease and sickness among the people.' Matthew tells how the news about Jesus spread all over Syria; how large crowds from Galilee, the Decapolis (the Ten Cities), Jerusalem, Judea and the region across the Jordan followed him.

As he writes, Matthew once again joins the crowd and listens to Jesus preaching the kingdom of heaven, and he remembers his longing to be part of it, for this was before he was called from his tax booth to follow the Lord:

One day the crowds were so large that Jesus went up on a mountainside and sat down and began to teach his disciples and the crowd what we now know as the Beatitudes:

'Blessed are the poor in spirit, for theirs is the kingdom of heaven.
Blessed are those who mourn, for they will be comforted.
Blessed are the meek, for they will inherit the earth.
Blessed are those who hunger and thirst for righteousness, for they will be filled.
Blessed are the merciful, for they will be shown mercy.
Blessed are the pure in heart, for they will see God.
Blessed are the peacemakers, for they will be called sons of God.
Blessed are those who are persecuted because of righteousness, for theirs is the kingdom of heaven.

Blessed are you when people insult you, persecute you and falsely say all kinds of evil against you because of me. Rejoice and be glad, because great is your reward in heaven, for in the same way they persecuted the prophets who were before you.'

(Matthew 5:1-12)

We tend to take words like meekness, compassion, purity of heart and peace-making as gentle and anodyne. Matthew knows well that they are quite the opposite. The Beatitudes, like so much of Jesus' teaching, are dynamite.

Matthew remembers the day Jesus taught them to pray. First he told them how *not* to do it. He said the hypocrites stood in the synagogues and on street corners where their piety could be seen, but this was wrong; the disciples should pray where they could not be seen, then God, who was not seen but was all-seeing, would reward them. They were not to use a lot of words, because God knew their needs even before they prayed to him. They were to say:

'Our Father in heaven, hallowed be your name, your kingdom come, your will be done on earth as it is in heaven. Give us today our daily bread.
Forgive us our debts, as we also have forgiven our debtors.
And lead us not into temptation, but deliver us from the evil one.'

(Matt 6:9-13)

As he writes, memories come flooding into Matthew's mind. He can hear Jesus' voice: "Do not store up for yourselves treasures on earth, where moth and rust destroy, and where thieves break in and steal. But store up for yourselves treasure in heaven, where moth and rust do not destroy, and where thieves do not break in and steal. For where your treasure is, there your heart will be also."

So many miracles too! Jesus calming a storm; Jesus healing the blind, the deaf and the lame; Jesus casting out devils: Jesus walking on the water; Jesus feeding several thousand people with just a few loaves and some small fish; Jesus even raising the dead to life.

And Jesus telling the most wonderful stories, parables they were called, teaching about the kingdom of heaven. There was one about a farmer who went out to sow seed, another about treasure hidden in a field, another about a merchant who sold everything he had to buy a perfect pearl; yet another – for the benefit of those disciples who were fishermen – about the net that caught all sort of fish and how they were graded; another about a woman who mixed yeast with her dough; another about a shepherd who lost a sheep and went looking for it, and one about a landowner who hired men to work in his vineyard. But Matthew's favourite parable is about a mustard seed. He can remember Jesus' exact words, and he writes them down just as he heard them all those years ago:

"The kingdom of heaven is like a mustard seed, which a man took and planted in his field. Though it is the smallest of all your seeds, yet when it grows, it is the largest of garden plants and becomes a tree, so that the birds of the air perch in its branches.' (Matt 13:31-32)

Lots of the stories were like that, difficult to explain, but somehow you knew exactly what Jesus meant.

One day the disciples asked who was the greatest in the kingdom of heaven. In reply, Jesus simply called a little child over, sat him on his lap and said, "I tell you the truth, unless you change and become like little children, you will never enter the kingdom of heaven. Therefore, whoever humbles himself like this child is the greatest in the kingdom of heaven." That stopped any further argument about who was going to be greatest!

Matthew puts his work aside. There is much still to do, but it can't be hurried. Every word that Matthew heard Jesus speak is etched on his memory. He must get it down, not only in proper order as an account of Jesus' ministry, but to convince people that he was the Messiah. Matthew will finish his Gospel with the words of Jesus after the Resurrection:

> "Therefore go and make disciples of all nations, baptising them in the name of the Father and of the Son and of the Holy Spirit, and teaching them to obey everything I have commanded you. And surely I am with you always, to the very end of the age."
>
> (Matt 28:19-20)

Sycamore Fig ~ (*Ficus sycomorus*)

Plant description

Zohary: 'The fig and the sycomore are representatives of the genus *Ficus* which comprises about 1,000 mainly tropical species. Unlike the fig, the sycomore is a robust tree, attaining the height of 10-15m and a crown circumference of 20-25m with a trunk sometimes 1-2m in diameter. Its leaves recall those of the mulberry but are shed only in extremely cold winters. Like many other tropical trees, it bears its fruit in grape-like clusters which spring from the main stem or the older branches, a phenomenon known as cauliflory.

'The syconia of the sycomore consist of a globular receptacle lined on its inner side with succulent hairs, among which the minute male and female flowers are inserted. At the top of the fig is a very narrow opening (ostium), encircled with tiny scales, through which certain wasps enter for purposes of oviposition . . . In the lower part of the fig are the female flowers, which are far more numerous than the males in the upper part near the ostium. The whole rather complicated story of pollination is not unlike that of the true fig tree. The fertilization of the sycomore by wasps is vital to the ripening of the fruit, but no seeds can be produced thereby, since the ovaries are converted into galls which make the figs inedible for man. To prevent the setting of this type of fruit, the ancient Hebrews incised the fig before maturity with a special knife. Such gashing is called *balos* in Hebrew, an operation to which the prophet Amos was presumably referring when he said: "I am no prophet, nor a prophet's son; but I am a herdsman, and a dresser of sycomore trees.' (Amos 7:14). Other countries used the same method, and Egypt and Cyprus, among others, do so still.'

Tom Ratcliffe adds some more detail about harvesting: 'The dressing of sycomore fruits occurs when they are almost at full maturity, but still hard and unripe. The labour is intensive, requiring total commitment and patience. The dresser climbs the tree and, with a sharp knife or fine spike, makes a small incision or puncture in each fruit. Within a matter of days the fruits mature and ripen ready for harvesting . . .'

Plant lore

Zohary also says of the sycomore, 'Some scholars assume that the species was introduced from Africa, perhaps by Natufian Man (about 10,000BC) bringing seeds or cuttings. This seems improbable because its fruit was not valued and could never have rivalled the fig, which thrives in the same area, the Coastal Plain. Although its timber was valuable, there is no evidence that it was imported into this country (The Holy Land).

'In my opinion, it was never in fact 'introduced' into Israel, but remained as a tertiary relic of the earlier tropical flora, not unlike other vestiges (*Accacia albida, Ziziphus spina-Christi*) which since the Natufian period have mainly been vegetatively planted and propagated from native stands . . .'

Ratcliffe again, throwing a more modern light on the reason it was necessary to go through all that performance to harvest a crop worth eating, albeit by the poor of the time: 'It would be fair to say that growers at the time of Amos and down to the beginning of the 20th century did not know what brought about such dramatic results. Maybe, long before Amos' day, an observant grower had noted that damaged fruits developed and ripened much faster, and were sweeter than undamaged fruits. So, without knowing exactly why, an additional task in the husbandry of sycamore fruits was adopted and passed down to successive generations.

'In the early part of the 20th century scientists found that Ethylene gas hastened the ripening of stored, green fruits such as oranges and bananas. Furthermore, it was also proved that the practice of incising and puncturing sycamore fruits released small quantities of Ethylene gas that lingered around the trees. A centuries-old mystery satisfactorily solved.'

Uses in modern herbal medicine

These will already have been explored with *Ficus carica*, the so-called 'true fig' in the Section on 'Chronicles'.

So, there we have it from the experts: The sycamore fig produces fruit after a most complicated pollination process by wasps; harvesting is labour-intensive; its fruit is inferior to that of the true fig in terms of nutritional value, and it bears a close resemblance to the mulberry in leaf and form. Amos tried to persuade God that he couldn't possibly be a prophet because he was only a humble dresser of sycamore trees.

However, because the sycamore fig develops a nice head of thick horizontal branches when left to its own devices, it was eminently suitable for the purposes of Zacchaeus, who climbed one in Jericho, and for whom life was never the same again . . .

ZACCHAEUS AND THE SYCAMORE FIG TREE
(Luke 19:1-10)

There is a child's hymn (author unknown) that goes:

'Zacchaeus was a very little man, and a very little man was he.
He climbed up into a sycamore tree, for the Saviour he wanted to see.
And when the Saviour passed that way, he looked into the tree and said,
"Now Zacchaeus, you come down, for I'm coming to your house for tea"

And that, broadly speaking, is what happened, although I doubt it was tea. It probably turned into quite a party.

Luke places Jesus' encounter with Zacchaeus in Jericho, a place identified by the lst century historian, Josephus, as 'a divine region, the fattest in Palestine'. Anywhere that fertile and desirable attracts wealthy inhabitants, and wealth is inevitably subject to heavy taxation. Zacchaeus had amassed considerable wealth himself. His climb to the top of his profession had certainly not been marked by honesty or by generosity. He was chief tax collector. He was what we, two thousand years later, would call a quisling – someone who collaborates with an occupying enemy to the detriment of his own people. Zacchaeus, a Jew, collected taxes from the Jews for the hated occupiers of his country, the Romans. He knew every trick in the trade and was familiar with advanced creative accounting, which provided him with a reliable source of extra income. Zacchaeus was a despicable creature; hated by those he milked; tolerated only by his own kind; friendless and no doubt lonely. That climb was to change his life irrevocably and for ever.

Jesus knew that Zacchaeus was in the tree and he called him down – one imagines with good humour – and invited himself and his disciples to Zacchaeus' house for a meal.

Such a burden fell from his shoulders at that moment that Zacchaeus, in a very public place with many witnesses, not only fulfilled the Jewish

Law for theft, but went well beyond it. Zacchaeus would have known the Law by heart, and he certainly recognized that it applied directly to him: 'The Lord said to Moses: "If anyone sins and is unfaithful to the Lord by deceiving his neighbour about something entrusted to him or left in his care or stolen, or if he cheats him, or if he finds lost property and lies about it, or if he swears falsely, or if he commits any such sin that people may do – when he thus sins and becomes guilty, **he must return what he has stolen or taken by extortion**, or what was entrusted to him, or the lost property he found, or whatever it was he swore falsely about. **He must make restitution in full, add a fifth of the value to it and give it all to the owner on the day he presents his guilt offering . . ." '** (Leviticus 6:1-5).

Also: 'The Lord said to Moses, "Say to the Israelites: 'When a man or woman wrongs another in any way and so is unfaithful to the Lord, that person is guilty and **must confess the sin he has committed. He must make full restitution for his wrong, add one fifth to it and give it all to the person he has wronged . . ." '** (Numbers 5:5-7)

There was a good deal of muttering from the crowd as Zacchaeus came down from the tree, but he stood up tall and said, **"Look, Lord! Here and now I give half of my possessions to the poor, and if I have cheated anybody out of anything, I will pay back four times the amount."**

'If I have cheated anybody out of anything' is enough of a confession of guilt to ensure that Zacchaeus must make restitution. Witnesses to that confession would have been only too pleased to make sure the contemptible tax collector kept to his promises. But Zacchaeus entertains Jesus in his home with a promise ringing in his own ears: 'Jesus said to him, "Today salvation has come to this house, because this man, too, is a son of Abraham." ' In other words, Zacchaeus, having repented, confessed, made restitution (or at least the promise of it), has been forgiven and restored to his rightful place as a son of God.

Spikenard ~ (*Nardostachys jatamansi*)

Plant description

Spikenard is a perennial herb belonging to the Valerian family. Ratcliffe says that this plant is native to the mountainous regions of Nepal and India, growing at altitudes of up to 4000m, that its leaves are entire (that is, without leaf stems), and that they arise from short, thick, hairy stems. Rose-pink flowers appear in clusters at the top of 10-20cm stems. All parts of the plant – foliage, stem and root – contain the highly aromatic oil, used as nard.

In biblical times nard was a most precious oil imported to the Holy Land via the spice route. It was valued by perfumers and used as an ingredient of incense in the Temple, but in modern times it has become almost obsolete.

Plant lore

There are several references to 'nard' in the Bible. In the Song of Songs the Beloved says: "While the king was on his couch, my nard gave forth its fragrance." (Song of Songs 1:12, KJAV). In St Mark's Gospel, an alabaster jar of the ointment was worth 300 denarii – the equivalent of an average workman's labour for 300 days. In St John's Gospel we read: 'Mary took a pound of costly ointment of pure nard and anointed the feet of Jesus and wiped his feet with her hair; and the house was filled with the fragrance of the ointment.' (John 12: 3 KJAV)

Uses in modern herbal medicine

The dried, powdered root of the aromatic Spikenard has been used in an infusion in the treatment of syphilis, 'rheumatism' and various skin diseases. Spikenard is often combined with other herbs (such as Dandelion and Burdock); in a syrup with Peppermint it makes a pleasant and effective remedy for colds and coughs. Spikenard acts as a blood purifier, improving general health and reducing fevers.

THE WOMAN WITH THE ALABASTER JAR

It is three years since Jesus left Nazareth and began his ministry. During that time he has chosen twelve of the most unlikely men to be his disciples; he has taught, healed, cast out devils and raised people from the dead; he has mixed with those considered to be the dregs of society and has been to some pretty merry parties with 'the wrong sort of people'. He has been castigated by Jewish rulers but has won the hearts of thousands of ordinary men and women. And throughout this time he has been followed by increasingly large crowds.

In such a life there has to be a place of sanctuary, a bolt-hole, a place of rest and relaxation. There is such a place in Bethany, just a few miles from Jerusalem, but its very proximity to the city is both convenient and dangerous. Jerusalem is the place where Jesus has taught in the Temple, where the scribes and Pharisees are plotting against him, this carpenter with his rabble of followers. His knowledge of the Law has confounded their arguments at every turn, and they are supposed to be the experts. They burn with furious impotence as they watch his enviable way with the crowds, his miracles of healing. But worse, people are hailing him as the Messiah, the chosen one of Israel. This cannot be allowed to go on.

In the house at Bethany live Lazarus (whom Jesus recently raised after he had been dead and entombed for four days) and his sisters, Mary and Martha. Mary is the quiet one; she is quite content just to be with Jesus, sitting at his feet, listening to him. Martha shows her love and concern by preparing good food and generally mothering him. This is where Jesus comes when he is tired and in need of some tender loving care. These people are his close friends.

It is six days to the great Jewish Passover Feast (four days before Judas Iscariot's betraying kiss and Jesus' arrest in the Garden of Gethsemane; four nights before Peter will deny him three times in the courtyard of the chief priest's house before the cock crows; five days to death by crucifixion on Golgotha). No doubt Jesus knows all this; his disciples do not, although they are aware of growing danger and they are becoming increasingly confused and anxious.

Traditionally, the woman with the alabaster jar of precious ointment is Mary Magdalene. In St Mark's account she is simply 'a woman', the implication being that her reputation leaves a lot to be desired. In St John's

Gospel it is Mary who lives at Bethany with her brother and sister. Are Mary of Bethany and Mary Magdalene one and the same person? We don't know, and it really doesn't matter. Let us stay with John's account in the NIV:

'Six days before the Passover, Jesus arrived at Bethany, where Lazarus lived, whom Jesus had raised from the dead. Here a dinner was given in Jesus' honour. Martha served, while Lazarus was among those reclining at the table with him. **Then Mary took about a pint of pure nard, an expensive perfume; she poured it on Jesus' feet and wiped his feet with her hair. And the house was filled with the fragrance of the perfume.**

'But one of his disciples, Judas Iscariot, who was later to betray him, objected: "Why wasn't this perfume sold and the money given to the poor? It was worth a year's wages." He did not say this because he cared about the poor but because he was a thief; as keeper of the money bag, he used to help himself to what was put into it.

'"Leave her alone," Jesus replied. "It was intended that she should save this perfume for the day of my burial. You will always have the poor among you, but you will not always have me."'

After Jesus is dead and in the tomb (very conveniently before Passover for the chief priests, the scribes and the Pharisees), and after the disciples have all fled for their lives, the house at Bethany is in mourning. Grief is mixed with fear since the chief priests are now looking for an excuse to kill Lazarus. The last thing they need is a living miracle reminding people of the works of Jesus of Nazareth.

The House at Bethany

In this place people come and go, speaking in whispers.
Martha cooks for those who will not eat;
Mary sits waiting for One who will not come;
Lazarus wishes he had not been raised,
And the fragrance of perfume lingers still.

(P.A. 'Passion Play')

Aloes ~ (*Aquillaria agallochum* – 'Eaglewood'. *Aloe vera*)

Plant description

Since there are varying opinions as to which 'aloes' have their references in different Bible passages, we must describe two vastly different plants: Ratcliffe says that *Aquillaria agallochum* is of the same family as the fragrant Daphnes, growing up to 35m. In Ratcliffe's opinion, four references to aloes in the Bible (that is, Psalm 45:8; the Song of Songs 4:14; Proverbs 7:17 and John 19:39) relate to the product of that tree.

Zohary thinks the tall Eaglewood tree, native to East Africa and northern India, in demand for its fragrance and oil, is undoubtedly that of 'aloes' in Psalm 45, but that as it appears in John as a perfume (and antiseptic) for shrouds it was probably an oil extracted from the succulent leaves of the *aloe vera*, widely used medicinally and for embalming in ancient Egypt and elsewhere. He says, 'It looks not unlike a small centaury plant with fleshy leaves forming a rosette. From the centre of this rosette a stem bearing a spike of reddish-green flowers arises annually.'

The Aloe (*Aloe vera*) grows wild in the tropics, but we know it better as an evergreen houseplant, when its necessary temperature can be assured. The succulent, spine-edged leaves are filled with a clear yellowish juice containing the bitter aloes. Cuttings root readily in pots of sandy, well drained soil.

Plant lore

The ancients used the juice of aloe vera mostly for embalming, medicinal and cosmetic purposes. Cleopatra is said to have relied on it for her wonderful complexion (no doubt in addition to her baths of asses milk). It was probably the Eaglewood Tree (*A. agallochum*) in Balaam's Third Oracle in Numbers 24: 6 . . . 'How beautiful are your tents, O Jacob, your dwelling places, O Israel! Like valleys they spread out, like gardens beside a river, **like aloes planted by the Lord**, like cedars beside the waters.'

Again, in Psalm 45:8, 'Your robes are all fragrant with myrrh **and aloes** and cassia.' And in the Song of Songs 4:14: 'nard and saffron, calamus and cinnamon, with every kind of incense tree, with myrrh and **aloes** and all the finest spices.'

In Proverbs 7, the wise father is warning his son against the adulteress, who comes to meet him dressed like a prostitute, with seductive promises. She says: 'I have perfumed my bed with myrrh, **aloes** and cinnamon. Come, let's drink deep of love till morning; let's enjoy ourselves with love! My husband is not at home; he has gone on a long journey . . .'

We shall look more closely at John 19: 38-42 in a moment.

Uses in modern herbal medicine

The clear sap (gel) expressed from the leaves of Aloe Vera is emollient to skin – a wonderful healer of wounds, inflammatory skin conditions, frostbite, exuberant scar tissue and of burns, even the more resistant burns resulting from radiation.

The cosmetic and healing properties of Aloe Vera were known in ancient Egypt and in biblical times, but recently even more wonders have been revealed by modern, more sophisticated research. Not only is Aloe Vera effective in the treatment of the herpes simplex viruses (I – cold sores; II venereal herpes), it has been suggested that the compound acemannon, found in Aloe Vera, may have an antiviral action which includes HIV. This being so, it is hoped that Aloe Vera will prove to have a place in the treatment of some cancers.

Used externally, Aloe Vera presents no problems, but combined with some prescription drugs (e.g. steroids and cardiac glycosides), there may be unacceptable side-effects. Internally, the gel works well inside the gut to heal peptic ulcers and, more recently, it has been found helpful in the treatment of Irritable Bowel Syndrome and ulcerative colitis. 'Aloes' is an effective tonic and digestive stimulant at low dosage, and laxative and purgative at higher doses

The Aloe Vera plant is grown so easily indoors that it makes an excellent first-aid kit for minor domestic accidents. One has only to snap off a leaf, express the gel and apply it directly to burn or graze or cut.

Flax ~ (*Linum usitatissimum*)

Plant description

The grace and apparent fragility of this most decorative herb gives no indication of the strength of its eventual uses. Flax is a hardy annual with a slender, straight stem and narrow, lanceolate leaves. It grows up to 60cm in height and from its erect stem branch delicate blue, five-petalled flowers which bloom from June to August. Flax is a sun lover; the more sun it can absorb, the more brilliant the colour of the flowers.

Flowers are followed by seeds, up to ten of which are enclosed in a capsule. To harvest the seeds, the whole plant should be cut down, the stems tied together loosely in bunches and hung upside down with the heads in a paper bag so that when the capsules dry and split the seeds are not lost.

The seeds are oleiferous (sometimes called linseeds, from which are produced a fine oil, rich in vitamins).

Zohary writes: 'Flax fibres for spinning, the linen thus produced, and the flax plant itself are the three meanings of the Hebrew *pishtah*. Since the word is mentioned several times in the Bible, flax must have been extensively cultivated . . .

'The Gezer Calendar, which was found at the ancient site of the city of Gezer, dating back to the beginning of the Israelite kingdom (c10th century BC), includes references to the cultivation of flax, which together with wool, was the chief material for weaving cloth for garments and linens.'

Ratcliffe gives a good description of the process required to produce linen. He says: 'Harvesting flax involves uprooting the whole plant. The long stems are carefully bundled together in sheaves, then set upright in stooks to dry, in much the same way farmers reaped their corn crops before the advent of the combine harvester. When the flax straw has dried, it undergoes a process known as "retting". The modern way of retting is to soak the straw in ponds, streams or specially constructed water tanks to promote decomposition and removal of the fleshy part of the stem. The retting process takes a week or two, depending on air temperatures. In biblical days, the straw lay on the ground or on flat roofs for weeks to expose it to cyclic wetting, drying, freezing and thawing; and although the retting process took very much longer, it was just as effective. The retted straw is then dried (Joshua 2:6) and crushed by rolling to facilitate the separation of the long fibre strands from the remaining fleshy part of the stem. The next process is called carding or hackling, the combing out of long straight threads ready for use in the manufacture of high quality linen (a reference to hackling, the combing out of flax can be found in Isaiah 19:9). Broken pieces of fibre, called tow, are not wasted, but used for the production of cheaper materials the poor can afford to buy . . .'

Plant lore

Flax is mentioned several times in the Bible: In Genesis 41:42, Joseph was dressed in fine linen at Pharaoh's court and given an exalted position after he had explained the king's dreams about the years of plenty and the years of famine in the land of Egypt.

In Exodus 9:31 (during the plague of hail in Egypt) we read: **'the flax and the barley were destroyed, since the barley was in the ear and the flax was in bloom.'**

In Exodus 35 we find listed all the materials used for the Tabernacle (the most holy place where the Ark of the Covenant was to rest) in the Sinai Desert, and these included 'fine linen' for the sacred garments for Aaron the priest and the garments for his sons when they served as priests.

In Leviticus 13:47 linen is mentioned in the regulations about mildew.

And there is that beautiful prophesy in Isaiah 42 of the Messiah who will come in mercy and justice: **'A bruised reed he will not break, and a smouldering wick he will not snuff out.'** In the KJAV 'wick' is translated as 'flax'.

The last reference to 'fine linen' is in Revelation 19:8 when the bride of the Lamb has made herself ready: **". . . Fine linen, bright and clean, was given her to wear." (Fine linen stands for the righteous acts of the saints.)'**

Pliny the Elder author of the many-volumed '*Historia Naturalis*', wrote: 'What department is there to be found of active life in which flax is not employed?'

Uses in modern herbal medicine

'Linseeds' are used as a demulcent laxative, taken from a teaspoon with water or added to breakfast cereal. The seeds also provide a fixed oil rich in Omega-6 fatty acids, essential for good health and now considered to be an ideal dietary supplement. Modern diets are often low in polyunsaturated fats (which it is thought may be a contributory factor in the development of chronic and even life-threatening disorders).

Linseed is used for the relief of recalcitrant coughs and may be used in the treatment of asthma. Linseed oil is rich in vitamins D (essential for strong bones and teeth) and E (essential for normal body cell structure and for the formation of red blood cells as well as for protecting vital tissues from pollutants. It is also said to slow ageing of cells.).

Linseed oil is good for the skin and can be applied to minor irritations and chafing. (And I know this has nothing to do with herbal medicine, but commercial standard linseed oil is wonderful for treating and rejuvenating starved and weathered wood!)

JESUS IS LAID IN THE TOMB

This, the fourteenth Station of the Cross, finds us with two men in a cold tomb, performing an act of love and reverence for someone they had admired and had hoped was the Messiah. They are not, as one might expect, from the dead man's family, or from his inner circle of friends. It is dangerous to have any association with this man, even in death, but something has driven them – one to supply the tomb, the other to bring fine linen cloth and a massive amount of mixed spices – driven them to a courage they had not been able to display before. They work together in silence over the broken body.

'Later, Joseph of Arimathea asked Pilate for the body of Jesus. Now Joseph was a disciple of Jesus, but secretly because he feared the Jews. With Pilate's permission he came and took the body away.

'He was accompanied by Nicodemus, the man who had earlier visited Jesus at night. Nicodemus brought a mixture of myrrh and aloes, about seventy-five pounds.

'Taking Jesus' body, the two of them wrapped it, with the spices, in strips of linen. This was in accordance with Jewish burial customs.

'At the place where Jesus was crucified, there was a garden, and in the garden a new tomb, in which no-one had ever been laid.

'Because it was the Jewish day of Preparation, and since the tomb was nearby, they laid Jesus there.' (John 19:38-42)

Who are these men, Joseph of Arimathea and Nicodemus? Nicodemus has been mentioned just once before (John 3:1-6) where we learned that he was a Pharisee, a member of the ruling council (the Sanhedrin), and that he came to Jesus by night. Jesus, remember, was a carpenter by trade, someone whose friends were low in the pecking order and not a very polished bunch: fishermen, tax collectors and prostitutes. But, in spite of his own high position, Nicodemus' greeting to Jesus was one of humility: "Rabbi, we know you are a teacher who has come from God, for no-one could perform the miraculous signs you are doing if God were not with him." No doubt Nicodemus came to Jesus under cover of darkness because he was afraid of being seen, but he was taught many things that night.

And Joseph of Arimathea? Also a Pharisee, also a secret disciple, and also afraid. However, he overcame that fear in his grief and asked Pontius Pilate for permission to take the body and to give Jesus a decent burial.

And so, here are two high-ranking Jews, Pharisees, members of the supreme court, exposing themselves to great danger. Why? Why, now that their hopes are dead? Jesus has been betrayed, denied, scourged, mocked and crucified. He is undoubtedly dead. His close disciples have all run away for fear the same thing might happen to them. The impossible dream of Jesus being the Messiah is over. Who can tell what they are thinking, but here they are, in the tomb, wrapping the body, with the spices, in strips of linen, in accordance with Jewish burial customs:

Take off your shoes as you approach the tomb, for this is holy ground.
See how tenderly Joseph and Nicodemus tend the broken body.
Watch them bind it in the winding sheet of grief, with myrrh and aloes
of despair.
Shed with them hot tears of shame at such a fearful, craven following.
They had so longed for him to be the Christ, the chosen one of Israel.
Defiant, brave at last, this one thing they must do: burial fit for the King
they'd prayed he was.
Soon a stone will seal the tomb, separate them for ever from their dream.
And yet, and yet, though all seems lost,
do they remember Lazarus?

(P.A. 'Passion Play')

We hear no more of Joseph of Arimathea and Nicodemus – their work is done and they have their place for ever in the Scriptures, but there is now the miracle of the empty tomb (John 20:1-9)

'Early on the first day of the week, while it was still dark, Mary Magdalene went to the tomb and saw that the stone had been removed from the entrance.

'So she came running to Simon Peter and the other disciple, the one Jesus loved, and said, "They have taken the Lord out of the tomb, and we don't know where they have put him!"

'So Peter and the other disciple started for the tomb.

'Both were running, but the other disciple outran Peter and reached the tomb first.

'He bent over and looked in at the strips of linen lying there but did not go in.

'Then Simon Peter, who was behind him, arrived and went into the tomb. He saw the strips of linen lying there, as well as the burial cloth that had been around Jesus' head. The cloth was folded up by itself, separate from the linen.

'Finally the other disciple, who had reached the tomb first, also went inside. He saw and believed.

'(They still did not understand from Scripture that Jesus had to rise from the dead.)'

After that, Jesus appeared to Mary Magdalene, who only recognised him when he called her by her name ('Jesus said to her, "Mary."'); then to the disciples in a locked room for fear of the Jews; then to Thomas, who had said he wouldn't believe unless he saw Jesus bearing the nail and spear marks for himself; then to the disciples by the Sea of Galilee, where he made them breakfast on the shore at daybreak.

John finishes his Gospel: 'This is the disciple who testifies to these things and who wrote them down. We know that his testimony is true. Jesus did many other things as well. If every one of them were written down, I suppose that even the whole world would not have room for the books that would be written.'

9 | Acts of the Apostles and Letters

If we did not have 'Acts' (The Acts of the Apostles) we would have no idea of the early Christian Church, other than information gleaned from the letters of St Paul. We would have no information about the way the Gospel was carried across the Mediterranean world – to Judea, the whole of Palestine and eventually to the heart of the Roman Empire.

'Acts' covers an approximate thirty-year period, from the gift of the Holy Spirit to the disciples gathered together in a house in Jerusalem at Pentecost, to Paul under close house arrest in Rome. 'For two whole years Paul stayed there in his own rented house and welcomed all who came to see him. Boldly and without hindrance he preached the kingdom of God and taught about the Lord Jesus Christ.' Paul was martyred in Rome about the year AD64, but Luke chooses to leave us with his friend and companion of so many dangerous adventures under armed guard in a house in Rome, still proclaiming the Gospel, unless, of course, Luke died first. That we don't know.

Luke, who wrote 'Acts' for Theophilus (see the introduction to 'The Gospels'), was a fine historian, but he is not writing a history as such here, nor does he attempt to give an exhaustive account of all that happened. That he was with St Paul on his missionary travels is without question, and he gives vivid descriptions of events and people at that time.

Peter is a leading character in 'Acts', but few of the other original disciples are mentioned, although we learn that James, the brother of John, was martyred under Herod quite early in the narrative.

Mark, the second Gospel writer, is still a young man in 'Acts' and his mother's house seems to have been the centre of the church in Jerusalem (Acts 12:12). Mark was related to Barnabas and so was taken as helper on a mission abroad, but for some reason Mark opted to return home. Paul was so enraged at Mark's behaviour that he refused to take him again, but later, when Paul is writing to the Colossians from prison in Rome, he tells them to receive Mark when he comes to them. And when Paul writes to Timothy, just before his death, he asks for Mark to be brought to him and he says, 'Only Luke is with me. Get Mark and bring him with you, because he is helpful to me in my ministry.' So whatever Mark had done to annoy Paul, he must have redeemed himself later.

In Acts, chapter 13, we meet once more Simon of Cyrene who was made to carry Jesus' cross on the way to Calvary, and his family and friends from North Africa, but we are not told how they came to be Christians. There are many gaps in this narrative, but the glimpses we get of the early Church are invaluable to us. It is in 'Acts' that we learn that followers of Christ were first called 'Christians' at Antioch, and we are shown how the Faith was given to the gentiles. 'Acts' is a most important book.

The Letters of St Paul

Paul was a wonderful letter writer: he taught (particularly about the Law and faith); admonished (often more in anger than in sorrow); was, at times, humorous; was always uncompromising, and was, sometimes, surprisingly gentle and tender (see I Corinthians 13, his great hymn to love so often read at weddings). Through his letters, we can add some details to the portrait of Paul as he is found in 'Acts'. There is always an immediacy about his writing and his actions; drama and great urgency are the norm for him. He wants people to come to Christ now, this minute. Looking back to Paul's own conversion, the great drama on the Damascus Road seems wholly appropriate for this man. Nothing less than a blinding light and a voice from heaven would have brought him to his knees.

Paul's post-conversion *magnum opus* was the conversion and integration of the gentiles so that all would know Jesus as Christ and Lord. He wasted no time and spent all his energy to this end, and we shall meet him in more detail with our herb 'Olive'.

Olive ~ (*Olea europaea*)

Plant description

There are some four hundred species in the Olive family, which thrive in temperate and tropical climates. The Olive tree grows slowly, rarely achieving more than 5m in height, but it is noted for its longevity. The Olive tree is evergreen with a distinctive gnarled grey trunk. Its lance-shaped leaves are grey on their under-surfaces and an attractive blue-green above. The Olive tree is more than tolerant of sparse conditions; it flourishes among rocks, on mountain slopes and on the poorest soil.

The sight of an Olive grove in full flower is breathtaking, but its springtime clusters of small white blossom are shed soon after pollination. The fruit is a one-seeded drupe, green in summer and bluish-black in its autumn maturity.

Cultivated Olive trees are kept pruned to facilitate harvesting by hand, when the trees are 'beaten' with long sticks so that the ripe fruit falls into waiting baskets.

Plant lore

Zohary says: ' The Olive leaf has symbolized peace and has heralded new life and hope ever since the early history of mankind, as so aptly expressed in the story of the Flood: **'And the dove came back to him in the evening and lo, in her mouth a freshly plucked olive leaf; so Noah knew that the waters had subsided from the earth.'** (Genesis 8:11)

'It was to this gnarled old tree that the other trees first appealed for reigning over them in the parable of the trees (Judges 9:8-9). The righteous as individuals and the integrity of the People of Israel were metaphorically likened, in the Bible, to this evergreen tree.

'So popular were the trees and their fruit that, apart from the daily diet, the oil was used in holy ointments of kings and priests, and for anointing the sick, for lighting at home and in the Temple, and as a solvent of various spices, incenses and aromatics used in perfumes and cosmetics.'

It seems that the Olive tree was the most useful of all the fruiting trees. The rich grain of its wood made it desirable for wooden ornaments and for decorative household utensils, as well as for high quality furniture.

When Solomon was building the Temple, two huge cherubim were carved from Olive wood to 'guard' the Ark of the Covenant in the inner sanctuary, and the doors of the inner sanctuary were also made of Olive wood. (1 Kings 6:23-33) And as for its legendary longevity, some say that the tree which supplied Noah's dove with its olive branch to signal the end of the Flood survives to this day (four thousand years or more). Certainly there are productive Olive groves in the Holy Land reputed to be a thousand years old, and Olive trees will still produce fruit when their trunks are quite hollow.

The Olive was part of God's Law dealing with justice and mercy (Deuteronomy 24:20), and this passage is so beautiful, and so relevant for us today, that it is worth us reading in full:

'Do not deprive the alien or the fatherless of justice, or take the cloak of the widow as a pledge, remember that you were slaves in Egypt and the Lord your God redeemed you from there. That is why I command you to do this.

'When you are harvesting in your field and you overlook a sheaf, do not go back to get it. Leave it for the alien, the fatherless and the widow, so that the Lord your God may bless you in all the work of your hands.

'**When you beat the olives from your trees, do not go over the branches a second time. Leave what remains for the alien, the fatherless and the widow.**

'When you harvest the grapes in your vineyard, do not go over the vines again. Leave what remains for the alien, the fatherless and the widow.

Remember that you were slaves in Egypt. That is why I command you to do this.'

Uses in modern herbal medicine

The Olive, like the Vine, had a considerable influence upon the lives of men and women in Biblical times; it still has in our day, and we know a good deal more about it now. We know that as a nutrient it provides essential fatty acids, so important in maintaining healthy nerve tissue, healthy skin and general wellbeing. In hot climates Olive Oil was (and still is) used for protecting the skin against damage from exposure to a strong Mediterranean sun.

Perhaps the ubiquitous Olive still has some secrets to reveal to us.

Certainly one of the more recent discoveries is that choline-like substances found in the leaves of the Olive tree exert a hypotensive action when taken and can be used in a natural way in herbal medicine for lowering elevated blood pressure to a more acceptable level.

THE ROAD TO DAMASCUS AND BEYOND

Our scene is set outside the city walls of Jerusalem, several years after the death of Jesus of Nazareth. A man called Stephen is about to be stoned to death, illegally by a lynch mob as it happens. He is about to become the first Christian martyr. This is holy ground. Stephen is a good man, one of the seven deacons of the early Church, whose particular responsibility has been to look after widows and orphans. But he has fallen foul of the religious authorities at a time of persecution of the early Christian Church. Some men were persuaded (paid) to say they had heard Stephen speak blasphemy, and so Stephen was seized and brought before the Sanhedrin, who produced false witnesses who testified that Stephen had spoken against the Temple and the Law.

Asked by the high priest if the charges against him were true, Stephen embarked on a whistle-stop tour through the Old Testament, quoting the great patriarchs, Abraham, Jacob, Joseph, Moses and King David, before bringing them up-to-date with Jesus, the Christ, the Son of God, whom they had murdered, as they had all the prophets.

Unwise? Yes, but Stephen is a man on a mission and nothing is going to stop him. To say that the religious authorities were not best pleased would be a magnificent under- statement. They shouted and raved; they rushed at Stephen and dragged him out of the city. They threw him down off the hillside and tossed great boulders on him. They won't rest until he is dead. But Stephen is not dead yet, and he is not repentant either. His face is radiant; he cries out that he can see Heaven open and his Lord standing at the right hand of God. He prays aloud, "Lord Jesus, receive my spirit." On his knees, he cries out, "Lord do not hold this sin against them", echoing Jesus' words from the Cross, and with this Stephen dies.

While all this has been going on, witnesses have laid their clothes at the feet of a young man named Saul, for safe-keeping. Saul hates these Christians and he thoroughly approves of Stephen's death.

In his play, 'Murder in the Cathedral', T.S. Eliot has his final *Chorus* say that the blood of martyrs and saints will enrich the earth and create holy places; that wherever a saint has lived, wherever a martyr has given his blood for the blood of Christ, it is holy ground. Even if armies trample over it, even if sightseers with their guide-books come to it, it will remain sacred, because 'from such ground springs that which forever renews the earth.' And so it was with Stephen, whose work as a deacon continues even today, and whose Feast Day we celebrate on the 26th December.

Stephen is carried off-stage, and we prepare ourselves for the next act, in which we meet Saul of Tarsus, tent-maker, Pharisee, bigot *par excellence.*

After Stephen's death things got even worse for the Church at Jerusalem. There was a great persecution and all Christ's followers (except the apostles) were scattered throughout Judea and Samaria, and as they scattered they preached the Word.

Chapter 9 of the Acts of the Apostles begins: 'Meanwhile, Saul was still breathing out murderous threats against the Lord's disciples. He went to the high priest and asked him for letters to the synagogues in Damascus, so that if he found any there who belonged to the Way, whether men or women, he might take them as prisoners to Jerusalem.'

Not a nice man, but look out Saul, you are in for a rude shock: Saul had almost reached Damascus when suddenly a light from heaven flashed around him. He fell to the ground. It was as though he had been struck by lightning. He distinctly heard a voice say to him, "Saul, Saul, why do you persecute me?"

"Who are you, Lord," Saul asked.

"I am Jesus whom you are persecuting," he replied. Now get up and go into the city and you will be told what you must do."

Flashing light; a voice from heaven; blindness. It took something that dramatic to take hold of Saul and to bring him to his knees. The men travelling with Saul were speechless; they had heard the disembodied voice, and they were frightened. They had to take Saul by the hand and lead him into Damascus, where he was blind for three days and unable to eat or drink, until God told a disciple called Ananias to go and to minister to Saul. This was not the most attractive proposition Ananias had ever had, and he told God so. He had heard of Saul and was sure this was a trap, 'But the Lord said to Ananias, "Go! This man is my chosen instrument to carry my name before the Gentiles and their kings and before the people of Israel. I will show him how much he must suffer for my name.'"

So Ananias did as he was told, no doubt with great fear and trembling. He found the house that God had shown him in a vision, and he found Saul in a very sorry state. He went in, placed his hands on Saul and said, "Brother Saul, the Lord – Jesus, who appeared to you on the road as you were coming here – has sent me so that you may see again and be filled with the Holy Spirit."

We are told that 'Immediately, something like scales fell from Saul's eyes and he could see again. He got up and was baptised, and after taking some food, he regained his strength.'

There were never any half measures with Saul. After just a few days with the disciples in Damascus, he was preaching Jesus as the Son of God in all the synagogues. People couldn't believe it. "Isn't he the man who caused havoc in Jerusalem among those who call on this name? And hasn't he come here to take them as prisoners to the chief priests?" Yet Saul grew more and more powerful and baffled the Jews living in Damascus by proving that Jesus is the Christ.'

The Jews, considering Saul the greatest turn-coat ever, conspired to kill him, but he eluded them by escaping over a wall in a basket let down by his new friends. When he arrived in Jerusalem, Saul tried to join the disciples there, but they doubted his sudden conversion and were afraid of him. It wasn't until Barnabas, a much respected member of the Christian community, introduced Saul to the apostles and explained what had happened and took charge of him that he was finally accepted.

In his second letter to the Corinthians (Chapter 5:17), Paul says, "Therefore, if anyone is in Christ, he is a new creation; the old has gone, the new has come!" This was most certainly true of himself. Saul, renamed Paul, became a missionary to the Gentiles. He was as passionate for Jesus as he had been against him. The prophesy made to Ananias in Damascus certainly came true – Paul did suffer for the Lord's name. He was arrested and thrown into prison (often), flogged (often), shipwrecked (several times), but nothing stopped him from spreading the Christian message. In particular, Paul, the Jew, became the apostle to the Gentiles, and through him the Gospel has spread throughout the world. Listen to his letter to the Romans (Chapter 11: vv 13, 16, 17, 18 and 24):

13. ' "I am talking to you Gentiles. Inasmuch as I am the apostle to the Gentiles, I make much of my ministry in the hope that I may somehow arouse my own people to envy and save some of them . . .

16. If the part of the dough offered as firstfruits is holy, then the whole batch is holy; if the root is holy, so are the branches.

17. **If some of the branches have been broken off, and you, though a wild olive shoot, have been grafted in among the others and now share in the nourishing sap from the olive root,**

18. **do not boast over those branches. If you do, consider this: You do not support the root, but the root supports you . . .**

24. **After all, if you were cut out of an olive tree that is wild by nature, and contrary to nature were grafted into a cultivated olive tree, how much more readily will these, the natural branches, be grafted into their own olive tree!" '**

Paul, called so dramatically on the road to Damascus several years after Jesus was crucified, who never actually knew the Lord in the flesh but believed 'by faith', and Peter, the fisherman, the rock on which the Christian Church was built, who knew Jesus intimately and who was present at all the defining moments in the gospels, worked together. They were both given new names. They both bore witness to Jesus as Lord. They were both martyred in Rome about the year 64AD. It is fitting that they should share a Feast Day – the 29th of June.

10 | Revelation
(Sometimes called the Book of the Apocalypse)

The Prologue to the Book of Revelation identifies the author as John, 'who testifies to everything he saw – that is, the word of God and the testimony of Jesus Christ.'

John is not high on some hallucinatory drug – although some of the visions shown him are so vivid and apocalyptic and terrifying that one might imagine so. He is writing at a time of great persecution for Christians, so that Revelation is a coded message to the churches. It is full of imagery and of symbols that would be recognised only by particular people. Animals, colours and numbers would all have been significant to those familiar with the Old Testament, but not to the Roman authorities. This book is a 'revelation' of what is to come: The Messiah will come in splendour and there will be a new Holy City (Jerusalem). This is a message in fantastic form of hope to strengthen Christians in difficult times; it tells them that they will be rescued from their trials and will have a glorious future.

Revelation is said to have been written either when Domitian was emperor (*c* AD55) or under Nero (c AD68). Some scholars give an even later date. But, like all Scripture, Revelation is not only for 'then', but for now also. There are still Christians being persecuted and martyred for their faith, and this is a message for them: Christ *will* come again; his kingdom is eternal; his love is unfailing and everlasting, and victory will be theirs.

We began with Genesis and have come full circle: In Eden, a river flowed out from the garden, and there was the Tree of Life standing in the middle of the garden. In the Book of Revelation (Ch 22:1-5) we read:

'Then the angel showed me the river of the water of life, as clear as crystal, flowing from the throne of God and of the Lamb – down the middle of the great street of the city. On each side of the river stood the tree of life, bearing twelve crops of fruit, yielding its fruit every month.

And the leaves of the tree are for the healing of the nations.

No longer will there be any curse. The throne of God and of the Lamb will be in the city, and his servants will serve him. They will see his face, and his name will be on their foreheads. There will be no more night. They will not need the light of a lamp or the light of the sun, for the Lord God will give them light. And they will reign for ever and ever.'

Amen

11 | Glossary

A

Abortifacient: Any substance which causes abortion.

Alkaloid: Alkaloids occur naturally in plants. The group includes nicotine, strychnine, morphine and its derivatives, atropine, caffeine and quinine. All are bitter. All have powerful effects on bodily function.

Allergy: Hypersensitivity to foreign substances (allergens) which come into contact with the body. These are most commonly grass or tree pollens, dust, mites, various foods and some metals. The body's response to these allergens manifests itself in many different ways: in skin reactions (weals; dermatitis), asthma or allergic rhinitis (hay-fever).

Alterative: A substance used to change bodily processes (in our context, to improve bodily function such as digestion or respiration).

Amino acid: Body protein breaks down into 20 different amino acids (basic 'building blocks' of body cellular structure). Essential amino acids are obtained from protein in the diet.

Anthelmintic: A substance used to kill or to drive out parasitic worms from the intestines.

Antimicrobial: Any substance which works against microbes – micro-organisms causing disease.

Antioxidants: Substances (e.g. vitamins C and E, manganese, selenium, and zinc) which prevent the oxidation of organic molecules and which are thus capable of 'mopping up' damaging free radicals which would otherwise damage DNA, protein and fat in cell membranes.

Antiprotozoal: Substances which work against protozoa (primitive, single-celled, microscopic animals, many of which are parasitic on humans), causing diseases, e.g. Malaria and Sleeping Sickness.

Antipyretic: A substance (or any other measure) which reduces fever.

Astringent: A substance which causes contraction of the tissues and therefore of value in stemming bleeding.

Ayurvedic: Of, or pertaining to Hindu medical tradition. (Veda = the ancient Hindu scriptures. Literally, sacred knowledge.

C

Carcinogen: Any cancer-causing agent.

Carminative: A substance which by relaxing sphincters allows the release of gases in the alimentary tract and thus relieves flatulence.

Cathartic: Purging of the bowels, particularly to rid the body of toxins.

Counter-irritant: Anything applied to the skin to provoke a mild inflammation to improve blood supply to the area to relieve deeper, more severe pain or to block sensory nerve impulses to relieve pain. (e.g. a Mustard poultice for bronchitis).

D

Decoction: Boiling down to obtain essence, or the resulting liquor from this process.

Demulcent: A soothing substance which forms a protective coating to mucous membranes (of the mouth or the gut) and which reduces irritation or inflammation.

Diaphoretic: A substance which promotes perspiration (and in doing so reduces fever and rids the tissues of toxins).

Diuretic: Anything which increases the output of urine.

DNA: Deoxyribonucleic acid (the self-replicating material present in all living organisms). DNA is a constituent of chromosomes, and chromosomes carry all our genetic information.

DVT: Deep vein thrombosis, which occurs mainly in the lower legs due to pressure and/or inactivity.

E

Emmenagogue: A substance which promotes or increases menstrual flow.

Emollient: A substance that soothes and softens the skin.

Endosperm: Albumen (protein) stored within the embryonic sac (seed) of a plant.

Enzyme: A catalyst in a living organism that is capable of producing chemical change in that organism, without itself being changed.

F

Febrifuge: Anything which reduces a fever.

Fixed oil: Oils which do not evaporate and which do not dissolve in alcohol, used as vehicles for essential oils which do dissolve easily and which are used in aromatherapy (e.g. Almond and Coconut).

Free radicals: Highly active groups of atoms which can be damaging to DNA and proteins and the fat in cell membranes. They are normally 'mopped up' by anti-oxidants. Free radicals are thought to be implicated in the formation of atherosclerosis (the build-up of fatty plaques in artery walls), in cancer, in rheumatoid arthritis and in many other conditions. They are said to be exacerbated by many agents, including radiation, pollutants and smoking.

G

Gluten: Gluten is the sticky protein constituent of wheat and rye that gives dough its consistency. Gluten is comprised of two proteins – gliadin and glutenin. Sensitivity to gluten causes intestinal mal-absorption (Coeliac Disease) which has to be treated by a strict gluten-free diet.

H

Haemostatic: Anything that stops bleeding (artery forceps, a tourniquet, cautery, or any number of substances which promote coagulation of the blood).

Halitosis: Bad breath. In most cases this is due to poor dental hygiene, to a malodorous diet or to smoking, but causes can include diabetes, kidney or liver failure or disease of the lungs.

Hepatic: Pertaining to the liver

I

Iatrogenic: Describes any condition that has been caused by medical treatment. (*Iatros* is Greek for 'doctor'). The causal factor may be unforeseen, accidental, negligent or simply an inescapable consequence of necessary treatment.

Infusion: Any fluid administered into a vein (other than blood which is always called a 'transfusion'). In herbal medicine it also refers to an extract obtained by soaking a substance in water (e.g. a teabag; leaves or seeds or ground root).

'in vitro': Biologically occurring, or caused to grow, outside the living organism – usually in a test-tube in laboratory conditions.

K

Keratin: Fibrous protein which forms the chief constituent of skin, nails and hair (also in feathers and horn).

L

Lactation: The period of milk production in a mother following birth. The action of suckling young.

Lactose: A disaccharide sugar (it contains two molecules, glucose and galactose) which is only found in milk. Lactose is used in food processing and in pharmaceutical manufacture.

Leucocyte: Any white blood cell – including 'polymorphs', eosinophils, basophils, lymphocytes and macrophages. The action of the leucocyte is to protect the body by producing antibodies against harmful substances or any invasive processes (e.g. infection).

Lipid: Any of a large group of fats and fat-like substances (including wax, oil, etc.) occurring in living organisms. Lipids are soluble in certain organic solvents, but are insoluble in water.

M

Mucilage: A gelatinous substance usually containing extracts of plants for medicinal purposes. It has the advantage of 'slipping down easily'.

Menorrhagia: Abnormally heavy and prolonged menstrual periods.

O

Omega-3: Polyunsaturated essential fatty acids converted in the body into substances which act as regulators for blood pressure, digestion, etc.

Omega-6: Polyunsaturated essential fatty acids found in vegetable oils. These are valuable in controlling cholesterol levels in modern diets high in saturated fats.

P

Pathogen: Any agent causing disease, particularly a micro-organism.

Phenols: Aromatic hydrocarbons which act as anti-oxidants (*see above) Phenols are used in household disinfectants too.

Phyto: A prefix which tells us that we are dealing with plants. Of plant origin (e.g. 'phytotherapy').

Prophylaxis: Precautionary action (treatment etc.) taken to prevent disease.

R

Rubefacient: A substance which reddens the skin by dilating blood vessels. Liniments sometimes contain rubefacients. (*See also 'Mustard')

S

Steroids: A large class of fat-soluble, organic compounds characterised by the number of nuclei in their carbon rings. Included in this class are the the adrenal cortex hormones, the sex hormones (androgens and oestrogens), progestogens, bile salts and sterols. These are natural steroids produced by various organs and released into the bloodstream under the governance of the pituitary gland. There is also a wide range of synthetic steroids – compounds produced for therapeutic purposes.

T

Tincture: 'Tincture' usually refers to colouring, but for pharmacological purposes we use it to describe a naturally occurring substance (often of plant origin) whose active constituents are carried in a solution, mostly in alcohol.

Thrush: Infection with the fungus *Candida albicans*. Thrush affects the warm, moist areas of the body – mostly the mouth and vagina. Characteristically, there is persistent itching and soreness from caseous (cheesy) white patches and raw areas between them. Babies, the chronic sick and the elderly often suffer from oral thrush – it just thrives on a milky environment when the mouth can't easily be cleaned.

Topical: A substance applied to the external surface of the body rather than taken internally or injected. These include ointments, eye and ear drops and poultices.

12 | Bibliography

Armstrong, Patricia. '*Passion Play*' Armstrong Publications, 2000.

Barclay, William. Commentaries on the Gospels and on The Acts of the Apostles from The Daily Study Bible series. Published by The Saint Andrews Press, Edinburgh.

Chevallier, Andrew, BA Hons, FNIMH. '*Phytotherapy. 50 Vital Herbs*' Published by Amberwood, 1998.

Ernst, Professor Edzard, MD, Ph.D. '*How Garlic Protects Your Heart*' Published by Amberwood, 1996.

Houselander, Caryll. '*The Kingdom of God*' from '*A Rocking-Horse Catholic*' Published by Sheed and Ward, Kansas City, MO 64141-6492.

Ratcliffe, Thomas H. '*Bible Plants, Fruit & Products*'. Published by Christian Year Publications, 2002.

Zohary, Professor Michael. '*Plants of the Bible*' Published by Cambridge University Press, 1982

HOLY BIBLES

Authorized King James Version (KJAV) Crown Copyright.

New International Version (British edition) Copyright: The International Bible Society.

The New Jerusalem Bible. Copyright: Darton, Longman & Todd and Doubleday and Company Inc.

OTHER BOOKS from AMBERWOOD PUBLISHING:

AROMATHERAPY

Aromatherapy – A Guide for Home Use by Christine Westwood. £1.99.
Aromatherapy – For Stress Management by Christine Westwood. £3.50.
Aromatherapy – A Nurses Guide by Ann Percival. £2.99.
Aromatherapy – A Nurses Guide for Women by Ann Percival. £3.50.
Aromatherapy – Simply For You by Marion Del Gaudio Mak. £2.99.
Aroma Science – The Chemistry & Bioactivity of Essential Oils by Dr Maria Lis-Balchin. £5.99.
Aromatherapy – Essential Oils in Colour by Dr. Rosemary Caddy. £9.99.
Aromatherapy – The Essential Blending Guide by Dr. Rosemary Caddy. £12.99
Aromatherapy Lexicon – The Essential Reference by Geoff Lyth and Sue Charles. £4.99.
Aromatherapy – The Baby Book by Marion Del Gaudio Mak. £3.99
Aromatherapy – The Pregnancy Book by Jennie Supper. £5.99

HERBAL

Ginkgo Biloba – Ancient Medicine by Dr Desmond Corrigan. £2.99.
Echinacea – Indian Medicine for the Immune System by Dr Desmond Corrigan. £2.99.
Herbal Medicine for Sleep & Relaxation by Dr Desmond Corrigan. £2.99.
Garlic – How Garlic Protects Your Heart by Prof E. Ernst. £3.99.
Phytotherapy – Fifty Vital Herbs by Andrew Chevallier. £6.99
Natural Taste – Herbal Teas, A Guide for Home Use by Andrew Chevallier. £3.50.
Woman Medicine – Vitex Agnus Castus by Simon Mills. £2.99.
Menopause – The Herbal Way by Andrew Chevallier. £5.99
Herbal First Aid – Natural Medicine by Andrew Chevallier. £3.50.
Plant Medicine – A Guide for Home Use by Charlotte Mitchell. £2.99.
Cancer – Herbs in Holistic Healthcare by Dr J. Walker. £15.99.
Herbal Medicine for Children by Frances Hambly. £6.99.

GENERAL HEALTHCARE

Insomnia – Doctor I Can't Sleep by Dr Adrian Williams. £2.99.
Eyecare Eyewear – For Better Vision by Mark Rossi. £3.99.
Arthritis and Rheumatism – The Sufferers Guide by Dr John Cosh. £4.95.
Feng Shui – A Guide for Home Use by Karen Ward. £2.99

NUTRITION

Causes & Prevention of Vitamin Deficiency by Dr L. Mervyn. £2.99
Vitamins ABC and Other Food Facts (for Children) by E. Palmer. £3.99
All You Ever Wanted To Know About Vitamins by Dr Leonard Mervyn. £6.99.

CALL FOR INFORMATION: **(01634) 290115**